Introduction to Kundalini Yoga and Meditation

Volume I

Begin and Deepen Your Practice

with the Kundalini Yoga of Yogi Bhajan

by Guru Rattana, Ph.D.

♥♥♥

Totally New Edition

Published by Yoga Technology, LLC

www.yogatech.com

websales@yogatech.com

PO Box 443, Sunbury, PA 17801

Phone: (570) 988 4680, Fax: (570) 988-4640

Editing and page layout by Chris Zook

Yoga drawings by Ann Marie Maxwell

Editorial Consultant: Siri Bandhu Kaur Khalsa

ISBN: 978-1-888029-14-7

Nothing in this book should be construed as medical advice. Always consult your medical doctor or licensed healthcare practitioner to ensure that the lifestyle changes and exercises are appropriate for your personal health condition.

Dedication

To Yogi Bhajan,

Father of Kundalini Yoga for the Aquarian Age

Kundalini Yoga

Kundalini Yoga is the uncoiling of the being.
It is the potential of creativity of the Infinite in the finite.
It is the widening of the behavior, and it is ultimate
happiness in life. It is super-humanly human.
It is intelligence.
It is grace.
It is utmost compassionate being.
It is classic Truth, which radiates in every facet of life.
It is a scientific technology which can be learned and
taught.
It is taught; it is not a momentary diversion to look
unusual or feel unusual.
It is the central nerve system we are talking about which
extends the grasp of the brain to imagine Infinity in its totality,
and then it is a gradual process to work
for that experience.
It is a scientific technology for happiness.

– **Yogi Bhajan**

Contents

When the pure psyche touches the bitterness it makes it sweet. When a wise man touches a fool, it makes him happy and wise. When a totally complete, comfortable happy man touches an unhappy man, he brings happiness. Life is a sharing. We share our sorrows and we share our happiness. And if somebody is in sorrow, and we pour our happiness into that person, we make him happy. For that we need clarity of mind. We need the strength of the soul. We need enlargement of our point of view. We need tolerance. We need courage.

Greetings from Guru Rattana

With a few precious exceptions, much of what was available when I discovered Kundalini Yoga in 1976 consisted of handwritten notes taken by a few of Yogi Bhajan's dedicated students. We treasured these notes because for many years there was no official note taking, audio recordings, or videos. I also arduously took notes at Yogi Bhajan's classes that I attended.

In the mid 80s, just after I had moved to San Diego, I gave an eager student free Kundalini Yoga classes with the agreement that we would work out a trade. The student, Ann Marie Maxwell, turned out to be the artist who made all the illustrations for my first four books (and most of the illustrations for this manual). In 1988 and l989, we enthusiastically put together the kriyas and meditations from my notes and from the sketchy early notes of other students.

We organized the kriyas and meditations into three themes. The first, and still the most popular manual, is *Transitions to a Heart-Centered World* (now in its second, substantially revised edition). The next was *Relax and Renew*, followed by *Sexuality and Spirituality*. *Introduction to Kundalini Yoga* contained our favorite sets from the first three manuals.

We crammed in as much as we could on each page. As a result, each of the first three books contains over 100 sets and meditations in just 200 pages. By the way, we formatted these on a typewriter that made justified margins. We found this rare machine in a used office supply store!

The present two-volume set now replaces the original *Introduction to Kundalini Yoga*. The purpose of this totally new manual is to explain in detail the basics of our Kundalini Yoga practice and to serve as a reference guide for new students, dedicated practitioners, and teachers of Kundalini Yoga alike.

After almost four decades of daily personal practice, teaching, and writing about this sacred technology, I can now share from my experience and address many questions and details about this rich and comprehensive technology.

My Personal Story

One question I'm often asked is how I got started. When I was 25 (1969), I came home from graduate school on vacation. My mom greeted me with great enthusiasm: "Guess what I have discovered?" "What?" "Yoga!" "What's yoga?"

She showed me three exercises: Cobra Pose, Bow Pose, and Locust Pose. I felt great! I did these exercises every day, and every day I felt great afterwards. For eight years, I practiced the new Hatha poses she taught me whenever I visited home. (She traveled around the U.S. to learn yoga, becoming the first yoga teacher in the Midwest and opening her own Self-Awareness Center in Evansville, Indiana.)

I did my yoga poses at the end of the day before I ate supper. As a result, I no longer had to rely on eating to try to recuperate from the day and get through the rest of the evening. With my yoga practice, I felt refreshed and available for activities during the evening hours.

When I discovered and gradually started practicing Kundalini Yoga in 1976, I felt even better. Why would I miss a day? I love feeling good! Kundalini Yoga introduced me to a new concept of when to practice — before starting my day. I began to notice that at about five o'clock in the afternoon, I wasn't as tired as before. I attributed this change in energy to my morning practice and especially Breath of Fire.

Just like my mom introduced me to Hatha Yoga, it was my sister, Guru Kirin, who introduced me to Kundalini Yoga. I had just returned from studying in Geneva, Switzerland, and was teaching at Dartmouth College in Hanover, New Hampshire. Guru Kirin came to visit that fall 1976. She told me she had met this amazing yogi in Boston and that the next time he was in town I must visit her and learn Kundalini Yoga. She showed me some exercises, including Spinal Flexes, which I added to my daily yoga practice.

In February 1977, Yogi Bhajan came to Boston for a lecture and to teach a weekend of White Tantric Yoga. In those days the courses were on Friday night, all day Saturday, and all day Sunday. I loved the experience and was impressed by the "yogi" who spoke very intelligently. I liked smart people, and this man had something that surpassed smart — he was "tuned in" and "turned on" in a way that I knew was very special, in fact, extraordinary.

The discovery and practice of Kundalini Yoga and Meditation has totally transformed my life in ways that I could have never anticipated or even known about when I began my practice. If someone had told me, "One day you will be a spiritual teacher," I would have responded, "What is that?"

I remember choosing my first meditation. The instructions said, "Practicing this meditation will change your life." I contemplated this statement for about a week until I realized that it could only change my life for the better. Somehow I trusted the technology to be authentic and beneficial. I have maintained that trust to this day.

I wish you the best on your personal journey.

Many blessings,

Guru Rattana PhD

May 2015

Foreword to 1989 Edition

For the first time in the history of the planet, the ancient secrets of personal transformation and fulfillment are available to all, regardless of education, social status, profession, income, religion, nationality, age, or sex. We are in an age of the "democratization of spirituality."

It is said that the science of Kundalini Yoga and Meditation was developed 50,000-70,000 years ago by rishis in India and Tibet, who systematically tested and perfected the precise movements, postures, sounds, and breathing patterns that activate different parts of the body and brain to produce specific results. Their goal was to develop a comprehensive method for humans to activate their fullest potential, creativity, and intuition in order to maintain healthy, vital bodies and to experience and dwell in the ecstasy of God consciousness.

Until recently, these secret teachings were passed from teacher to selected students who underwent intensive tests and trials. The student was then given one meditation only, which had to be mastered (in 10-12 years!) before he (the teachings were reserved for men) could begin to practice another. Kundalini Yoga, which incorporates many yogic teachings, was brought to the West and presented to the public for the first time in 1969 by Yogi Bhajan. Not only was this the first time Kundalini Yoga had ever been taught publicly, this was the first time it had been written down and made available to all who desire to practice.

We are living at a critical juncture in planetary evolution. The survival of the planet and the human species depends upon nothing less than a healing transformation of consciousness. It is not surprising that Kundalini Yoga, one of the world's most powerful tools of transformation, should again appear to facilitate personal change and empower us to effect social change.

The practice of spiritual disciplines such as Kundalini Yoga contributes to global healing in two ways: (1) As individuals release fear, anger, hatred, and conflict and experience confidence, faith, love, acceptance, and peace, the collective consciousness is transformed. (2) Conscious, balanced, and heart-centered individuals are able to, and choose to, make conscious, balanced, and loving decisions in their personal, business, social, and political lives.

It is my observation that most of us already have enough information about "What's the matter?" with the planet and ourselves. We are motivated and deeply desire change! What we are looking for now is the means to effect change and actually experience a difference — inner peace and grace; living a truly happy, fulfilled, and creative life; and making our contribution to creating a sustainable, equitable, and peaceful world. The technology of Kundalini Yoga and Meditation was designed to empower us to do our job. Even a small dose offers relief from stress and gives us the feeling of hope and access to powerful energy. Dedicated practice offers lasting experiences of joy, peace, empowerment, and health.

As a teacher, it is my observation that Kundalini Yoga invariably works! I have never had a student who did not immediately experience noticeable changes in well-being. And I have often been surprised at how little a new student had to do to get results from chronic problems such as back pain and insomnia. Kundalini Yoga is a generic technology that can be combined with counseling and self-therapies for reaching the highest human potential and accomplishing our personal empowerment and spiritual goals.

I have studied the popular issues of the age: co-dependency, healing the inner child, relaxation and stress reduction, self-empowerment, weight-reduction, maintaining youth and beauty, self-love and esteem, and overcoming addictions, fear, depression, and anger. Kundalini Yoga gives one the mental power, physical stamina, and emotional balance to deal more effectively with all these issues. It changes the neurological and chemical balance in the body and brain that triggers these problems in the first place. And best of all, it makes you feel good, happy, alive, and comfortable in your body.

Kundalini Yoga belongs to everyone. It is a gift to humanity. Never before in the history of the planet have so many possibilities for radical change been so accessible. The challenge today is not to climb a mountain to see a yogi in a remote cave to receive a secret meditation. The test today is to have the grit, courage, and will to take the first steps and then commit to change. The challenge is to practice the available technology. As Yogi Bhajan is famous for saying, the challenge, and the blessing, is to KEEP UP.

The essence of free will is that we are at choice. We can choose between mediocrity or self-empowerment. Self-empowerment cannot be bought or given to us. It can be read about, thought about, and taught in a seminar, but personal transformation is a participatory sport! It only works if you are in the game. And it is more fun to be in the game. The rewards come when we play. So get in the game and bring your friends. The more players, the better. It is a win, win game. You win, the world wins. Play ball!

Gururattan Kaur Khalsa
1989

P.S. Yogi Bhajan always said that he was here to train teachers, not to gather students. He considered everyone in his classes teachers, or potential teachers. He used to teach a Kundalini Yoga set and then tell us to go to the park, put up a "YOGA" sign, and start teaching the set. He assured us that the students will come.

Summary Contents of Volumes I and II

Introduction to Kundalini Yoga and Meditation is a reference guide on the basics of Kundalini Yoga and Meditation to serve beginning students, committed practitioners, and teachers. ***Volume I: Basics to Begin and Deepen Your Practice*** offers a comprehensive explanation of the fundamentals of Kundalini Yoga as brought to the West by Yogi Bhajan. This manual describes in detail the techniques used to awaken the Kundalini, including

- The locks or bhandas
- Pranayama or breathing
- Posture and an open heart
- Mantras and meditation
- Kriyas/yoga sets designed to deliver specific effects

It includes the basics beginners must learn and perfect as they continue their practice through the years, including

- Understanding the mind and meditation
- Guidelines for practicing Kundalini Yoga
- How to design your personal practice
- Tips to optimize your progress

You will find kriyas and meditations to deal with stress, addictions, depression, insomnia, spinal health, mental clarity, activating your navel center, and opening the heart. You will discover how to direct your attention and guide your inner journey to health and happiness.

Volume II: Inner Guide to Awareness and Self-Initiation explains the physiological, mental, and energetic aspects of the awakening process and how to evolve from ego to soul consciousness. This manual examines two basic systems that help us understand our energetic make-up and the process of enlightenment: (1) *The 10 Body System and Numerology* defines the human awareness mechanisms and the path of the soul. (2) *The Chakra System and the Elements/Tattvas* identify our life challenges and how to develop our powers and gifts. There are also discussions on

- The dynamics of daily sadhana
- The phases of spiritual awakening
- Mantras, meditations, and finding your guru mantra
- Activation and refinement of your inner sensory system
- How to be your own therapist in dealing with your human issues

This manual is designed to help you optimize and embrace your personal journey and lead you to experience self-love, inner peace, and oneness with all.

Welcome to Kundalini Yoga

You are blessed to find the powerful transformative technology of Kundalini Yoga, brought to the West by Yogi Bhajan. Even a modest practice of 20-30 minutes a day will create significant changes in your life.

- ♥ You will feel more energized, more relaxed, and more alive.
- ♥ Your awareness will increase, allowing you to notice life's nuances and opportunities that once escaped you.
- ♥ Your presence will become more magnetic, clearing the way for you to move out of the pain and struggle mode of living and into the attraction mode of being.
- ♥ You will tap the courage, acquire the will, and cultivate the inner strength to deal with life challenges in a whole new way.
- ♥ You will become more authentically *you*.

You are about to embark upon a journey of consciousness and discovery of your Soul Self.

There Is Something for Everybody!

Kundalini Yoga and Meditation offers something for everyone, regardless of age, level of experience, body type, or physical condition. Don't be intimidated by the pretzel poses you see on the covers of yoga magazines, online, or in the media. If you wish to feel good about yourself and improve the quality of your life, Kundalini Yoga is for you!

This technology is for anyone who wants to relieve stress, to be happier and more relaxed, to feel better, and to become more empowered and more conscious. Being out of shape is a good reason to begin, not an excuse to avoid the feeling of well-being that awaits you. If you can breathe, you will benefit. Kundalini Yoga is not a competitive sport or a beauty contest. This practice offers you ways to feel more alive, to take care of your body, and to love yourself and your life.

You are invited to jump in and get started. You will be surprised and delighted at how easy it is to begin your practice and increase your sense of well-being. This manual explains in detail what to do and how to direct your attention. Once you have a handle on the basics, you may wish to refer to the chart in Appendix II for a list of exercises, yoga sets, and meditations listed according to functions, effects, and difficulty.

Part I: Yoga of Awareness

1. Benefits of Practicing Kundalini Yoga and Meditation

Kundalini Yoga and Meditation offers many benefits to everyone who practices this powerful technology.

Health and Healing

Health: As our body systems are cleansed and strengthened, we enjoy more vibrant health, tap into abundant energy, and are able to operate at a more functional level.

Cleansing: As we cleanse our physical, mental, and emotional bodies, we are able to release sabotaging attitudes and beliefs, giving us space to acquire beneficial new habits and behaviors, and we experience a lighter, purer, more authentic state of being.

Healing: As we heal ourselves on many levels, our presence has a positive impact on others and our environments. Our touch, words, and smile uplift and heal.

Releasing addictions: Kundalini Yoga is a healthy, legal, and easily available means to satisfy our deep craving for spiritual satisfaction and love. Kundalini Yoga can thus help release our addictive urges for substances and behaviors that can harm us. Once we experience what feeling good really feels like, we want more! We can practice anytime, as much as we want, for free!

Strengthening Our Electromagnetic Field

Our physical, mental, and emotional health are revealed by the strength, coherency, and stability of our aura, or the electromagnetic field, surrounding our body. Yogi Bhajan says that a healthy aura is bright and extends about nine feet in all directions.

A strong, coherent, bright aura allows us to be more present in our relationships with others and to deal more effectively with our life challenges. We are able to disassociate from negative circumstances and to project positive, elevated energy to improve them. With the development of our electromagnetic field, our sense of well-being improves, and we become more balanced and creative human beings.

All Kundalini Yoga practices amplify our electromagnetic field. Our sensitized aura serves as an integral part of our inner guidance system. It alerts us to dangers and protects us from negative forces. Synchronized with our soul and universal energies, we can allow our plans to change to avert danger, and we are more receptive to opportunities as they present themselves.

A Great Way to Live

The practice of Kundalini Yoga and Meditation builds our mental, physical, emotional, and spiritual capacity to meet our life challenges from inner strength and to more fully enjoy our life.

The optimization of all our body systems (1) reduces stress; (2) produces physical, emotional, and mental stamina and endurance; and (3) facilitates the transition from an emotionally reactive existence to living in the sensitive awareness of higher consciousness. In sum, it is possible to live life in a whole new way.

Problem Solving

There is no way to avoid the challenges of human existence, but we can be more effective in handling life's tests. By broadening our perspective and by tuning in to our emotions as messages from our soul, we can intuitively and instinctually know the best course of action and make wise choices. Connected to our inner guidance system, we can operate from self-knowing and self-confidence instead of being a victim.

Opportunities and Elevated Attitudes

As we awaken our meditative mind, we are able to transcend the conflict generated in our analytical mind. We acquire new attitudes about life, our self, and the world. We are able to trust, to be grateful, to not take things so personally, and to live with fewer expectations and judgments (and thus fewer disappointments).

These elevated attitudes unleash our ability to manifest and draw opportunities to us. We no longer feel the need to manipulate, struggle, or fight for what we want. We accept our life challenges as opportunities to learn and grow. As we embrace our self and our life, we are able to access our special talents and operate from our highest potential.

Life Is a Miracle and a Gift

As we become more conscious, we are able to perceive life as a gift and a miracle — a series of synchronistic events unfolding at the right time and place, in a constant flow. We release our need to micromanage every detail, because discovering and accepting life as it unfolds is much more interesting, fruitful, fun, and real.

Joyful and Meaningful Living

With expanded awareness, life becomes rich, meaningful, entertaining, and fulfilling.

Spiritual Gifts

Our spiritual path offers us many gifts:

- **Happy** — We feel content and are happy to be experiencing our unique life.
- **Clarity** — We attain mental clarity and focus. It is easier to act fearlessly, finish tasks, and be truthful, fair, and honest.
- **Intuitive Knowing** — We tap into and are guided by our intuitive knowing and feeling of what is right and best. We are no longer tormented by the mental conflict that feels the need to control and to figure everything out.
- **Higher Awareness** — Through meditation, we establish an intimate relationship with our soul and the Divine within, which opens us up to more soulful relationships with others.
- **Universal Connection** — The congruent alignment of body, mind, and spirit opens channels to subtle, non-physical dimensions of existence. Our mind awakens to the Universal Mind.
- **Prayer Power** — Clarity, humility, and devotion to a higher power clear the channels for our prayers to be received and answered.
- **Impacting World Peace and Becoming a Force for Change** — The more we elevate our consciousness and the quality of our personal energy and inner space, the more we positively affect the world and those around us. Our inner peace contributes to creating world peace.

The Yoga of Fulfillment

We are tapping, through consciousness, the Supreme Consciousness. It is not a subconscious process. There will be no miracles, tricks, or a denial, for this is the Yoga of Fulfillment.

The first qualification for Kundalini Yoga is that you seek that awareness. We will not get rid of the ego. For that matter, we will not deny anything in us. We will expose the ego and make it universal!

We will not sit and beg softly that we may someday find God. We will make ourselves so strong and pure that God must come and look for us and look after us.

God has got your number … let him look you up!

1971

2. *The Technology of Transformation*

A Unique Combination of Techniques

Kundalini Yoga is an ancient technology designed to cultivate the expansion of consciousness through the awakening and raising of Kundalini energy up the spine. This is accomplished by

1. Activating and opening the energy centers, called **chakras,** along the spine.
2. Mixing and uniting **prana** (life force) with **apana** (eliminating energy), which generates pressure to awaken the Kundalini and cause it to rise.

All forms of yoga have the same goals: (1) awakening to soul consciousness, (2) accessing spiritual energy, and (3) uniting human consciousness with Universal Consciousness, the Divine Source, or God. Yogi Bhajan said Kundalini Yoga works 16 times faster than Hatha Yoga. We have no way (or need) to prove the numbers, but it is true that the practice of Kundalini Yoga produces results very quickly, which is due to the fact that it combines all aspects of the various traditional yoga practices, including:

Hatha Yoga — physical asanas

Raja Yoga — meditation to awaken the higher mind

Mantra, Japa, or Naad Yoga — repetition and chanting of sacred sounds

Pranayama — breathing and breath awareness

Bhakti Yoga — devotional prayer, meditation, and chanting

Karma Yoga — service

Tantric Yoga — union and balance of the polarities

Even though the various aspects of Kundalini Yoga appear to be similar to other yogic practices, the approach, practice, techniques, benefits, and results of Kundalini Yoga (as shared by Yogi Bhajan) are different from other systems. Kundalini Yoga is a unified system that operates with a unique dynamic. Its integration of many yogic techniques produces an awakening in consciousness that supersedes the results possible from the individual techniques alone. By regularly practicing Kundalini Yoga, we develop a radiance and depth of awareness very quickly. Dedicated practice generates a purified force field within our mind and energy bodies that make it possible to experience an awakened state of consciousness whereby we become aware of our Soul Self and the presence of the Infinite/Divine within.

Modern Yogis

Many yogic practices in the past required isolated environments, such as an ashram or monastic setting. Such traditional yoga practices also focused primarily on a withdrawal of the senses, with the intention of disconnecting from and transcending the physical body and escaping from the physical world. Both the focus and approach of Kundalini Yoga are radically different.

Rather than requiring one to renounce worldly affairs, the practice of Kundalini Yoga is geared toward householders, living within society and in a community. Instead of trying to escape the karma of relationships, children, and earning a living, the goal of Kundalini Yoga is to bring dharma, or spiritual living, into all aspects of human life.

Acceptance and enjoyment, *not* denial and rejection, of our body and our earthly journey are our goals. Instead of trying to shut down our sensory system, we turn our sensory awareness inward. By shifting our attention away from external distractions to inner self-focus, we can consciously connect with the energetic dynamics of our soul in our physical and emotional bodies. With increased awareness, we are better able to enjoy our humanness. We upgrade our physical experience and function better in the world.

How Kundalini Yoga Creates Transformation

Kriyas

Kundalini Yoga as shared by Yogi Bhajan consists of kriyas of one or a series of exercises whose components and sequence are designed to produce effects that are greater than the sum of their parts. "Kriya" literally means "work" or "action."

Each kriya is a special combination of (1) exercises or postures (asanas), (2) breathing (pranayama), (3) hand and finger positions (mudras), (4) spinal alignments called locks (bhandas), and (5) sacred sounds (mantras), which together and in their prescribed sequence create specific effects.

The kriyas work simultaneously with all the systems of the body, including the circulatory, pulmonary, endocrine, muscular, immune, nervous, and reproductive systems. The synergy of breathing techniques, postures, rhythmic movements, mantras, and attentive awareness produces powerful transformational effects. Here is what happens:

- Pressure on a specific area or system of the body causes the blood to saturate that area.
- The capillaries, cells, and organs in the areas being stimulated discharge their impurities and toxins into the bloodstream.
- Our body is revitalized and rejuvenated as impurities are eliminated, the blood and body organs are purified, and the blood flow increases.
- The pressure and increased blood flow impact the glandular system, causing the glands, which are associated with a specific chakra, to secrete their specialized chemicals, or hormones, awakening the energy center in that area.

- The activated areas, and the body as a whole, begin to build a charge — an increase in pranic energy.
- The pranic charge, or voltage generated by the exercises and amplified by the glandular secretions, awakens nerve pathways (called nadis) throughout the body.
- The purification and activation of all the body systems, the strengthening of the nervous system, and the increased electric charge all prepare us for the gradual awakening of the Kundalini.

We can think of our body as like a car with many battery cells (glands) working together. Each of our human batteries, similar to a car battery, is made up of water and chemicals. The voltage of each battery increases with a higher concentration of chemicals. The chemicals in our body are secreted by our glands. Our glandular secretions enhance and maintain the voltage in the body. (This is why it is said, you are as young as your glands.)

Awakening the Kundalini

Raising the Kundalini

Every human being contains an incredibly powerful storehouse of soul energy symbolized as a sleeping serpent, coiled 3.5 times, at the base of the spine ("kundal" means "curl" or "coil"). Once awakened, it uncoils and ascends through the spinal column to the crown chakra at the top of the head, triggering a transcendent spiritual state of awareness.

By practicing the technology as set out by Yogi Bhajan, the raising of Kundalini energy happens gradually. Yogi Bhajan often told us that it is not difficult to raise the Kundalini. What is difficult and requires continuous work is keeping it up, i.e., maintaining and living in higher consciousness. For Yogi Bhajan, what matters is our increased awareness and ability to live conscious lives.

Experiences of raising one's Kundalini vary widely. It is possible to experience Kundalini as heat or a liquid flow in the spine or to see it as brilliant light. Whatever the individual experience, it is usually a pleasant and even euphoric sensation.

Shaking, twitching, and other forms of uncontrolled movements are *not* the result of Kundalini rising. These movements of energy are indicators of (1) cleansing, (2) release of stress, and (3) a weak nervous system that must be strengthened to integrate the higher frequency Kundalini energy into our system.

Gradual Awakening

Spontaneous Kundalini awakenings can occur among practitioners of certain disciplines that try to forcefully raise the energy without preparing the physical body and nervous system to hold higher frequency energies. When the physical body is not strong enough and/or is affected by the use of recreational drugs, spontaneous Kundalini arousals can result in trauma or mental disturbance.

Spontaneous awakenings can also occur in people who have never practiced Kundalini Yoga and have no idea of what is happening. There is no way to predict or control this phenomenon. However, we can prepare our body and nervous system to accommodate this potent energy. Kundalini Yoga as given by Yogi Bhajan prepares our body to integrate the energy as it is being slowly released.

It is important to reiterate that awakening our Kundalini through Yogi Bhajan's Kundalini Yoga is a gradual and often imperceptible process. Yogi Bhajan warned us to avoid seeking the glitter and to focus on achieving an expansion of consciousness and living with a compassionate heart.

The Powerful Effects of Practicing Kundalini Yoga

The progressive and systemic transformation resulting from regular practice of Kundalini Yoga occurs because of the following changes in our physical and energetic systems.

- All our body systems are cleansed, activated, and balanced, which results in an integrated interaction of all physiological and energetic systems. This creates a sense of peace, wholeness, and well-being.
- The electromagnetic voltage of our body/mind is progressively amped up. As a result, our auric field becomes lighter, clearer, stronger, and more magnetic.
- There is a gradual strengthening of the nervous system and opening of our chakra centers. As a result, we feel more alive, whole, protected, and empowered.
- The increased voltage throughout our body, the activation of the glands to secrete their specialized chemicals, and the strengthening of the auric field have holistic, expansive, and balancing effects on our mind, emotions, and body.
- As the body's energy channels gradually open, our mind, body, and emotions become receptive to and infused with higher frequency Universal Energies.
- These channels then become available to carry the gradual activation of the Kundalini — the powerful energy of our soul. This happens as both the pranic energy (the life force generated from the combination of breathing and other techniques) and Kundalini energy increase and are diffused throughout our being.

As a result of all of the above, we experience increased creativity, vitality, clarity of mind, emotional balance, radiance, and an *awakening of consciousness.*

Profound Shifts with Kundalini Yoga

The interactive dynamics of the various components of Kundalini Yoga create profound transformation.

Raising Our Frequency and Purifying the Subconscious

Our physical and energetic bodies store the energetic imprints of beliefs, thoughts, and attitudes about our identity, others, and the world. These subconscious programs are hidden from our conscious awareness.

When we vibrate at lower frequencies (with fear, anger, anxiety, and sadness), our mind's focusing and attention mechanism is co-opted by the darkness (lack of light) of the imprints in our subconscious. Controlled by subconscious programming, we are sucked into reactive thoughts and driven by embedded compulsions and behaviors. We engage in self-criticism and have a poor self-image and low self-esteem.

With the practice of Kundalini Yoga, the electro-chemical balance of our body increases to bring about a system-wide vibratory frequency that is higher, brighter, more coherent, and more subtle. As the lower frequencies are upgraded, the electromagnetic radiance increases throughout and around our body. In other words, our aura becomes more coherent and our radiance gets brighter.

As our frequency increases, it becomes easier for our mind and body systems to let go of tension and to relax. The subconscious storehouse of impressions encoded in our physical and emotional bodies begins to dissolve, as the fear and anger stored in our body tissues, which constrict our organs and muscles, begin to release. As this process continues, we naturally and progressively let go of old ways of being and become available to experience higher states of awareness.

Awareness, Letting Go, and a Shift in Identity

As the grip of our subconscious loosens, the vibrations of fear and anger that separate our awareness from the Infinite and our soul gradually disappear.

As our subconscious imprints are released,

- Our sense of identity becomes less linked to negative impressions and thoughts.
- We feel a sense of peace and freedom, and experience a lightness of being.
- Our sense of identity as an energetic presence of light becomes clearer and more available in our awareness.
- We progressively react and relate differently to others and to our life challenges.

As we become more aware and continue to let go, we undergo a profound shift in consciousness:

- We increase our ability to stay inwardly self-focused.
- Our awareness deepens and becomes more subtle and refined.
- We refine our self-concept to include subtle attributes that make us feel more authentic, accepting, and kind toward ourselves.
- We begin to perceive our self as an energetic being of Love and Light — a radiant field — which we recognize as our soul.

A Different Relationship with Your Questions

It is normal for beginners to have many questions. When your thinking mind is in charge, you want specific answers and explanations about how things work and why. You believe that answers to your questions will bring you peace. But your mind continues to generate more questions, and your inner conflict is not attenuated. What you really need is a different relationship with your questions. What you really want is resolution and inner peace, which are available in your heart.

When you start your practice, it is advisable to write down all your questions and put this list away. The practice of Kundalini Yoga and Meditation will awaken in you another way to find answers to your questions. You will receive answers from within. You will learn to listen within instead of searching outside yourself. Through your own personal experience, you will graduate from trying to figure everything out to trusting your intuitive soul knowing.

The answers you receive may not be what you expect, but expectations get in the way. The cleanest way to find answers is to be in "discovery mode," making yourself available to listen, to receive, and to find guidance in whatever form it appears. All the above become available as your awareness expands. So focus on your practice and awakening, be patient, and stay alert. The Universe and your soul speak to you in many interesting and unexpected ways.

Just forgive, excel, and lead with grace to leave a legacy of kindness and compassion.

How Change Happens

Change happens because energies move. Our personal transformation happens when energy patterns shift in our mind and in our physical, emotional, and subtle bodies. We don't get rid of "bad" or "negative" energy. We increase its frequency and create coherency so that it expresses differently in our being. Kundalini Yoga and Meditation practices modify energy in the following ways:

Move Energy
We move energy so that blocked or repressed energy gets unstuck and vital pranic energy can flow and nurture all parts of our being.

Activate and Awaken
We activate and awaken dormant energies so that asleep energies become available for use, i.e., we tap our creative potential and awaken our light.

Raise Frequency
We raise the frequency of energies so that they can be expressed in elevated ways.

Infusion
We infuse higher vibrations into our energy field by chanting mantras. As a result, our being resonates with and receives support from the Universal Field.

Alter Patterns
We break up habitual patterns, create new circuitry, and imprint new patterns in our being. As a result, we are able to shift our perceptions, thoughts, responses, and behavior.

Integrate
We integrate the energies that are both activated in our body systems and become available from cosmic sources by relaxing, letting go, feeling, and enjoying their presence in our body.

Redirect
We redirect energy so that we can use it more productively and become empowered human beings. We no longer live as a victim but as a conscious co-creator of our own lives.

3. Mind and Meditation

To understand how Kundalini Yoga and Meditation creates shifts in our consciousness, we must first understand how our mind works. The human mind has three basic channels: (1) the dualistic channel, (2) the neutral channel, and (3) the subconscious channel. (This topic is discussed in more detail in Volume II.)

1. Our *rational or dualistic mind* performs functions necessary to make choices. It is able to evaluate, compare, contrast, and analyze options and information. Without a neutral arbitrator to help us make choices, however, our dualistic mind fluctuates between negative and positive thoughts and creates in a state of conflict and confusion.

2. Our *neutral mind* gives us the faculty of non-judgmental observation from where we are able to transcend our dualistic mind and focus our awareness on reality beyond intellectual concepts and thoughts.

3. Our *subconscious mind* is beyond our conscious knowing and control. Our subconscious programming is always in the background influencing how we think and feel.

Normally we operate almost exclusively from our *dualistic channel* or "rational" mind, which is constantly emitting thoughts. Yogi Bhajan says our mind emits 1,000 thoughts per wink of the eye. In other words, our mind is programmed to automatically think.

Our rational mind has the capacity to analyze, compute, calculate, and perform other thinking functions, which make it possible to evaluate our life situations and what to do about them. By default, our dualistic mind is influenced, usually controlled, by our subconscious mind or programming.

The neutral channel, our meditative mind, liberates us from the thinking, analyzing, and judging activity of our dualistic/rational mind. It also has the power to liberate us from our subconscious programming. It does so by connecting us to our intuition and to our peaceful inner space, where we are able to consciously connect with the Infinite and our soul. Our neutral mind is thus our access route to non-physical reality and where we can experience inner peace, stillness, and non-judgment/neutrality.

In sum, we escape the endless chatter and conflict in our dualistic mind by accessing our neutral mind, where we can listen to our intuition — the voice of our soul. *Changing channels from our dual mind to our neutral mind is a most basic goal in our spiritual practice. It is our inner foundation that makes all of our other goals possible.*

Change Channels in Your Mind

If you have been discouraged by the chaos in your "monkey mind," know that you are not alone and that there is hope. It is impossible to experience silence or peace in your dualistic mind where you constantly hear your thoughts and replay your neuroses. So any instructions that say "clear your mind" without teaching you how to access your neutral mind will just create frustration. The trick to experiencing a state of inner silence and peace is to change channels from your dualistic mind to your neutral mind. The neutral mind is your non-dual channel. It has only one voice — not many. When your neutral mind is an available partner, your dualistic mind can actually compute rationally. Contemplative meditation is possible when your neutral, meditative mind is awakened.

Preparing for Silent Meditation

In Kundalini Yoga, the physical exercises prepare us for meditation. There are many meditative practices. The ones most commonly used in Kundalini Yoga are chanting mantras out loud, reciting mantras silently, and pranayama, with and without silent mantra. These techniques can actually be considered preparation for contemplative meditation. They awaken our mind and body so that we are able to turn our attention inwards to our neutral channel. We can enjoy silent meditation after practicing these powerful techniques that clear the subconscious mind, enabling us to access the qualities of silence, stillness, and peace in our inner space. The meditation techniques help us to achieve a calm, sensitive, non-emotional, and alert intuitive space where we can relax, surrender, and be renewed. Consistent meditative practice promotes inner peace, happiness, and the ability to live life in neutral awareness or higher consciousness.

Mantra Meditations

Most of the Kundalini meditations use sacred mantras, usually chanting with a tune or reciting the sacred sounds in a monotone. The sound current of the divine mantras embodies the qualities of the Universal Field. Repetition of these sacred sounds releases negative imprints and harmonizes the flow of elevated energy and prana throughout our physical and energy bodies. Devotional chanting activates and infuses our human vessel with the infinite frequencies and uses the energy of our emotional body as glue to merge our finite being with our infinite essence.

Eye Focus

During most meditations, the default eye focus (called *dristi*) is at the third eye, which is located in the center of the forehead just above the eyebrow line. Focusing here causes the optic nerves of our two physical eyes to create a pressure or sensation at the third eye, which indicates its location. Yogi Bhajan said looking at the tip of the nose is the most powerful way to activate the pituitary gland.

Meditation instructions often include gazing at the tip of the nose (which creates mental balance) or toward our chin (which helps balance the emotions) with the eyes very slightly or one-tenth open. The other benefit of keeping the eyes one-tenth open is that it keeps us from spacing out and helps us stay more present in our body.

Attention and Awareness

We cultivate the faculty of awareness with eye focus, as explained above, and by training our mind to pay attention to the sensations in our body and spine, a chakra, the breath, a mantra, or parts of our physical body being activated by an exercise. As we train our mind to focus and practice awareness,

- We discipline our mind to serve instead of manipulate us.
- We access the pure, still, stable space in our neutral mind.
- We awaken our inner sensory faculties.
- We acquire the capacity to direct energy.
- We experience physical, mental, emotional, and spiritual well-being.
- We access expanded levels of consciousness.

Beginning and Ending a Day

My friend, learn never to wake up without meditation or without thanking your own unknown — your God. And never sleep without meditation and relating to your own unknown, God, who knows if tomorrow shall come. Keep the account clear. Start the day with God, see the day with God, and then God will take care of it. Isn't that simple? And at the end of the day, give yourself to God and sleep. If the morning dawns on you again, get up and live!, moment to moment, day to day, and walk away with the precious gift of life. Life is a precious gift!

July 14, 1975

4. Basic Techniques of Kundalini Yoga

The powerful effects of Kundalini Yoga are achieved through the interactive dynamics of the following aspects and techniques, which will subsequently be described in more detail.

- ♥ Postures and Angles
- ♥ Rhythmic Movement
- ♥ Stretching without Straining
- ♥ Pranayama — Conscious Breathing
- ♥ Bhandas/Locks
- ♥ Mantras
- ♥ Deep Relaxation
- ♥ Personal and Group Practice

♥ Postures and Angles

Kundalini Yoga is the yoga of angles. Each angle produces a specific effect. If the arms are to be held at 60 degrees, they must be held at 60 degrees (not at some other point from 45 to 90 degrees) to activate the full effect of the exercise. Each posture creates a stimulation, cleansing, and strengthening of our many body systems.

The angles and movements of the postures put pressure on different centers and systems of the body, causing blood to saturate these areas. Within a matter of minutes, the revitalized blood circulates into the areas that are under the contracting or expanding pressure brought about by these active postures.

♥ Rhythmic Movement

Many Kundalini Yoga exercises are active and use rhythmic movement to create the effects, including a sense of dynamic flow. In some exercises, like Cat-Cow, you may wish to begin slowly in order to fully engage the moving parts of the body and spine and to find your personal rhythm. Going slow initially also allows you to be aware of the movement of prana and the building and strengthening of your electromagnetic field.

♥ Stretching

It is important to ***s–t–r–e–t–c–h*** as you establish a posture. For example, when the arms are held up at 60 degrees, stretch the fingers, shoulders, and arms to open the armpits. By stretching, you will discover that the exercise becomes easier and achieves its full physiological effect. The stretching and breathing greatly facilitate holding a position for a longer time. Instead of your body parts feeling like dead weights, you vitalize each area and your whole system.

Stretch but Do NOT Overextend, Overexert, or Strain
Care should be taken to never overexert or strain. Stretching or extending only part way within your comfort zone will enable you to do more with time. You will find that what you can do at first, for only a few seconds or for a minute, will progressively become easier, and you will gradually be able to do the exercises for longer periods of time.

Avoid Tension
Keep the parts of your body not involved in the exercise as relaxed as appropriate. To allow the energy generated by the exercise to flow directly into the areas being stimulated, they must not be stressed. Tension prevents the body from fully absorbing the energy being generated.

♥ Pranayama

Various kinds of powerful breathing techniques in Kundalini Yoga super charge and vitalize our blood, nerves, and other body systems. Focused and powerful breathing is often combined with various postures, mudras, and mantras. Paying attention to our breath and how it is breathing in our body is an effective way to build body/mind/energy consciousness. Coordinating the breath and the movement, with attention to what is being stimulated, increases the activation and the experience after the exercise.

♥ The Locks/Bhandas

Bhandas, or locks, which are part of most Kundalini Yoga exercises, consist of delicate alignments of the muscles and the position of the body and spine, with the intent to facilitate the flow of energy. Adjusting one's posture and lightly squeezing the muscles around the spine create alignment and pressure so that the Kundalini can move freely up and then down the spine. The locks are applied after the completion of the active portion of a Kundalini Yoga exercise. Lighter versions of the locks are sometimes used during the exercises and pranayama. Learning the bhandas properly when beginning your practice is critical (see page 41 for more information).

♥ Mantras

Mantras are sounds that are encoded with the qualities and essence of divine frequencies. The silent and vocalized repetition of mantras or sacred sounds is an integral part of our Kundalini Yoga practice.

The most basic instruction for the breathing, or pranayama, during an exercise is to mentally listen to the sound of SAT on the inhale and integrate the sound of NAM on the exhale. The recitation of other specific mantras are part of certain exercises, the result of which enhances the effect of the kriya. In faster breathing like Breath of Fire, we may choose to mentally chant SA TA NA MA.

Mentally listening to and reciting mantras clear the subconscious and train the mind to be attentive. After preparing the body with physical exercises, the sounds of the mantras resonate more easily throughout the entire body. In addition, the combination of silently reciting mantras and doing an exercise amplifies the voltage in our body, which helps the body resonate at higher frequencies.

♥ Deep Relaxation

After a kriya, we allow the body to go into a deep relaxation. This gives time for all the energies in the body to adjust, release, align, and integrate the effects of the kriya. A new level of increased vitality is reached, and we become aware of a deeper and lighter inner and outer radiance. The deep relaxation after a kriya is at least 5 minutes and often 10 to 15 minutes.

♥ Group and Personal Practice

Kundalini Yoga consists of both personal and group practice. Our personal practice gives us the space to design a sadhana to work with our own issues and energy. Group practice synergizes the group energy. Our collective alignment adds another dynamic, which facilitates moving from individual to group to Universal Consciousness. In both situations, alone and with a group, we learn to focus on our self and cultivate awareness skills.

Active and Passive Aspects of Kundalini Yoga

How we practice Kundalini Yoga helps us become more aware and facilitates letting go of past conditioning. To maximize the benefits of our practice, it is critical to understand that *each Kundalini Yoga exercise has both an active part and a passive part.*

The *active part* is the actual performance of the posture, movement, breath, locks, and recitation of the mantras. The *passive part* is the relaxed space between exercises and at the end of a set. The integration of the effects of each exercise takes some time to complete. Therefore, *the passive aspect must be experienced for the exercise to achieve its full benefit!*

During the passive space between exercises, or a series of exercises, and at the end of the kriya, we simply let go and allow our body to relax and integrate the effects of the exercise. If the exercise is done sitting, we usually stay in the sitting position after the exercise. If the exercise is done on our back or stomach, we relax in these positions. During the deep relaxation, we are on our back.

"Doing nothing" releases resistance and allows relaxation and letting go. We stay present to the sensations in our body. We may be aware of an "electric/magnetic radiance," which grows, expands, and deepens with each subsequent exercise that makes up a kriya. The passive time gives the body the space to

- Integrate the localized effects of the exercise throughout the whole body
- Bring all our body systems into balance and harmony
- Allow the increased electrical/magnetic charge to strengthen our nervous system and consolidate our aura or electromagnetic field

We take advantage of the passive moments to cultivate awareness and to enjoy the results and benefits of the work we have done.

Duration of Passive Period

The amount of time for the passive period depends upon the duration and intensity of the exercise, but usually a minimum of 30 seconds to one minute is required. Early on, Yogi Bhajan taught that the passive part of a Kundalini Yoga exercise should be as long as the active part.

To determine the appropriate time for the passive part, we can pay attention to the time it takes for our body and breath to come back to a normal rhythm. The normalization of the breath is a good indicator of how long the body takes to circulate the secreted chemicals and to integrate the effects of the exercises. It is also interesting to note that it takes about one to two minutes for our blood to make a complete circuit through the body.

We can also pay attention to the sensation of aliveness and radiance circulating through and around the body. A stable, grounded, in-the-body sensation can indicate that the balancing and integration is complete.

SICKNESS: Most sickness comes because you listen to negativity. Protect the self — don't indulge in negative conversation.

March 11, 1970

5. Tailoring Your Practice to Your Level and Schedule

In this chapter, we discuss tips to optimize and customize your practice to meet your time and body requirements.

Warm Ups

There is a warm up set on page 97 that can be done before any kriya or meditation. You may also pick certain exercises as warm up exercises to complement the kriya you are doing. For example, if the kriya is all done in Easy Pose, you may wish to do leg stretches to prepare.

Basic Rule

The basic rule for practicing Kundalini Yoga kriyas is to do the exercises in the specific sequence and combination specified. You can shorten the times of the individual exercises to fit them into your schedule (see below) and to accommodate them to your physical condition, but the rule of thumb is to proportionally reduce the time of each exercise. However, for shorter exercises, do not go under one minute or so, as this amount of time is needed for the activation to happen. Performing 26 repetitions of an exercise will also fully stimulate the body.

Timing of Postures and Exercises

In most cases, the time or number of reptetions given for each exercise corresponds to the duration Yogi Bhajan gave when he taught the exercise in class. It generally indicates the time to achieve full activation and results. You can work up to the specified time, adjusting it to your ability. You can also substitute counting repetitions for the time. For example, 1 minute (depending on the exercise) many be equal to 26 repetitions. 2 minutes may approximate 54 repetitions.

Be aware, however, that the times given by Yogi Bhajan when he first taught the sets many years ago were often quite long. (The kriyas in my original four manuals were all taught by him before 1988.) What I have noticed is that in the early years, we needed to do exercises longer to achieve the same effects that we can achieve in shorter times now. The energy was so dark and dense on the planet that it often took a Herculean effort to break through to the Light.

Our goal is to generate and move energy to effect healing and to create lasting health benefits and structural shifts in consciousness. The amount of time this takes depends on many factors, most of which are neither measurable nor predictable, such as the tenacity of our resistance, the depth of our wounds and programming, and our willingness and ability to change. Fortunately, growth is both ongoing and cumulative. So as Yogi Bhajan is famous for saying, "Keep up!"

If You Cannot Perform a Posture or Exercise

If you are physically unable to do an exercise or can do it for only a very short time, there are several options that help maintain the full integrity and effects of the kriya and that facilitate actually doing the exercise as your body gets stronger and more flexible.

- Isometrically move the muscles that you would use to perform the exercise. In other words, you can strengthen the muscles with subtle movements, such as by slowly contracting, holding, and then releasing them, which can be repeated for the duration of the exercise. You can also visualize yourself doing the movements. Be sure to use the designated breathing patterns.
- If you can only do an exercise for a short time, maximize its effects by applying the locks, focusing your attention on your body, and breathing powerfully. Concentration on a mantra and/or the breath can make performing a pose easier.
- When necessary, substitute exercises that produce similar results but are easier for you to do.

Beginners are not expected and, in fact, are warned not to overexert themselves or to try to press beyond their current capacity. Work up to the longer times, focusing on activation, by slowly and progressively strengthening, stretching, and flexing the muscles needed to perform the exercise. For leg stretches, if necessary, loop a strap or towel over your feet to maintain straight legs. Do not bend your knees to reach your toes.

Do Your Best

It is not necessary to do a posture or movement perfectly to produce a result. Although we do our best to perform the Kundalini Yoga exercise correctly to stimulate and activate the body systems, we carefully adapt to our body's capability and gradually work up to longer times and better postures. Stress and strain block the flow of energy.

Comfort Level Touchstones

Given that the primary goal of Kundalini Yoga is to activate and move energy, it is important not to exhaust yourself. The amount of time for doing an exercise that is appropriate for your body can be determined by observing three basic principles: (1) avoiding overexertion, (2) doing what's comfortable, and (3) continuing until a breakthrough occurs.

Overexertion

You experience overexertion when you go beyond your personal physical limit. At that point, your muscles start to tense up, and you create stress in order to complete the exercise. You thus use up, instead of generate, energy, sometimes feeling drained or depleted. You then have to recuperate afterwards to get your energy back. When you use muscles that are not prepared, they get sore and ache, your kidneys get tired, and sometimes you even hurt yourself.

Comfortable

Comfortable means doing an exercise for a length of time that feels good. There is no overexertion. You enjoy a harmonious rhythm and comfortable pace. Optimally, the time specified in the kriya's instructions will fall in this category, and you will experience the full effects and benefits of the exercise.

Breakthrough

You experience a breakthrough when, at a certain point, you realize that you have passed a threshold. Something has happened. Your energy has shifted. During the passive period after the exercise, or during the deep relaxation at the end of the set, your energy moves to another level of aliveness. You feel refreshed and renewed. Optimally, you can do each exercise long enough to cause your glands to secrete so that you experience a shift in awareness and a transformation of energy.

Our goal is to generate and move energy to create a breakthrough, not a breakdown.

Length of Session

The length of your set will vary depending on how long you do the exercises for and how much passive time you spend between exercises. Here are some other important factors to consider when devising a set that fits your schedule.

- As noted above, the times of the individual exercises can be reduced to fit the time you have available. In this way, harder sets can also become more manageable for beginners. It's worth repeating that the best way to shorten the time of longer sets is to *proportionally reduce the length of each exercise*. There are cases, however, when other variations are more appropriate. For example, you may choose to reduce the time of exercises that are initially too taxing for your body.
- Tuning in will add a few minutes. If possible, add silent time to be with yourself.
- The deep relaxation after the set should last an additional 5 to 10 minutes.
- Tailor your Kundalini Yoga practice times so that you do not feel rushed. The more relaxed and present you are to what you are doing and what is happening, the better the results will be and the more awareness you will cultivate.

Consistent Practice Produces Results

If you have one to two hours per day to devote to your practice of Kundalini Yoga, you will achieve striking results! If you have less time, consistent practice also produces great results. Gradually build your practice. Kundalini Yoga and the spiritual path are rich and rewarding. Over time, you can make a lot of progress.

Shorter Sessions

If you wish to meditate, but do not have time for a full kriya, warm up the spine first with Spinal Flexes or do some other exercises of your choice to prepare your body. The length of a session depends on how much time you have and the results you want to achieve. No excuses — do something even if only for five minutes before you start your day.

A Student's Story

Here is the experience of one male student, who had a very early morning appointment and had to reduce the times for each exercise:

> This morning I did each exercise for just over half of the time I had done them previously. I found I was able to spend much less time recovering from overexerting myself before tackling [note the aggressive verb] the next exercise. As a consequence, I raised as much energy as I had previously with the extended times. My idea now is to remain at this level and gradually build up as my fitness and stamina improve. It feels better to exercise at a level that I can manage easily rather than to push myself to the limit and have to spend so much time recovering from each part of the set.

Experiment and Experience

You begin your Kundalini Yoga practice by learning how to effectively execute (1) the postures, (2) the locks, (3) the various breathing patterns, and (4) by familiarizing yourself with the basic mantras.

After you feel confident that you are doing the exercises correctly, pay attention to what you are feeling in your body. In other words, after your mind is satisfied that it knows what you are doing, move your awareness to your sensory experiences.

During and after each exercise and meditation, monitor what is happening in your body. It is your job to pay attention to the effects of an exercise and to enjoy the results! Your touchstone is "experiment and experience."

Tune in to Yourself

Your Kundalini Yoga practice is about you! Before your yoga practice, take a moment to "tune in to yourself" — feel the sensations in your body and be with your breath.

Cultivate Awareness and Allow Integration

After each exercise, feel the effects in your body and allow the energy to align and flow. Each exercise generates its own specific effects, so relax and permit the integration to happen before going on to the next one.

Your Body Is Your Guide

As you become sensitive to your body, you will know when to stop and when to press on. If you move as your awareness indicates and rely on your own sensitivity, you can maximize the benefits and prevent overexertion and possible injuries.

Don't Force, Be Kind

Never practice with an attitude of beating yourself up. You are not in a battle. Practice with the goal of improving your health and cultivating inner peace. Being kind to yourself releases tension. Everyone was a beginner once, and everyone has his or her own limits and strengths. With consistent practice, improvement can happen much faster than imagined.

Women and Menstrual Cycle

During their moon cycle, women are advised not to do strenuous abdominal exercises, including leg lifts, Stretch Pose, Breath of Fire, and Sat Kriya, and inverted postures like Shoulder Stand. Women need to focus on grounding and not on raising energy during their moon cycle, which is more of an inner meditative time than an active time. However, it is important to move the energy in the lower chakras. Cramps are caused by stuck energy. Even walking and gentle leg exercises can help keep your energy moving and prevent discomfort. Adjust the level of your cold showers during your moon cycle. Be sure to end with some level of cool to not feel sluggish.

Kundalini Yoga has to be understood. There is reserve energy in us, which has to be uncoiled. It is pure, passionate, precise, and piercing. Add anything you want to add. Every individual has his or her freedom in the Kingdom of God and the domain of Mother Nature. Every creature has to create environments to find the exalted self.

6. Basic Sadhana Guidelines

The most basic aspect of Kundalini Yoga is sadhana — our daily spiritual practice. Below we discuss the basic guidelines to help you maximize the benefits of your Kundalini Yoga practice and to create your own personal sadhana.

When

Ideally, it is best do your sadhana (daily spiritual practice) early in the morning (around 4 a.m. or 5 a.m.), 2½ hours before (and during) sunrise in the "ambrosial hours." However, if you are unable to arrange your schedule to get up this early (and get enough sleep!), start your practice later. (You may notice that you need less sleep.) But daily practice *before* you start your day is prescribed and produces the best results.

Conditions

If possible, practice in a clean, quiet place that is reserved for your spiritual practice (away from electronic equipment like computers and cell phones). Approach your practice with reverence, dedication, and gratitude. Enjoy and take full advantage of this precious time to be with yourself and to nurture your soul.

Food in Belly

For maximum effectiveness, practice at least an hour after eating a light meal or two hours after a substantial meal. You need energy and the ability to concentrate to do Kundalini Yoga, so you don't want to be hungry and thinking about food. But when your stomach is full, you are distracted and cannot optimize your practice. Obviously you won't have eaten a meal before morning sadhana. A few almonds (or other very light snack of your choice) ten or so minutes before your practice may be needed to sustain your body.

What to Wear

Wear clean white or light-colored clothes of natural fibers (cotton, wool, silk) that are reserved for this purpose. White is recommended because white reflects all the colors and brightens the aura. Avoid black, because it absorbs all the colors and reduces the radiance of the aura.

Hair Tied Up and Covering Head

If your hair is long enough, tie it up on the top of the head to focus your mental energy and stimulate the awakening of your crown chakra. Covering your head with white cotton cloth also helps retain the natural energy from your hair, aiding your ability to focus, meditate, and contain your energy.

Bare Feet

Unless your feet are really cold, bare feet are recommended, because that allows energy to flow in and out through the soles of the feet. Your skin is the biggest organ and needs to breathe freely. There are 72,000 nerve endings that correspond to the different organs/parts of the body that are stimulated more effectively when barefoot. Being barefoot also gives you greater traction while performing standing asanas and helps you feel grounded and connected with the Earth.

Sequence

The recommended morning routine is as follows:

1. Do some wake up exercises or Breath of Fire (in or out of bed) to get you going.
2. Take a cold shower (or end a warm shower with cold to stimulate blood flow to the capillaries).
3. Sit down on your mat and take a few minutes to be silently present to your breath and feel the sensations in your body.
4. Tune in with the Adi Mantra: ONG NAMO GURU DEV NA MO.
5. Do warm up exercises of your choice.
6. Perform your chosen kriya.
7. Deeply relax.
8. Meditate.
9. Enjoy silent time with yourself.
10. Conclude with a prayer, closing song, and three long SAT NAMs.
11. Do some standing grounding exercises if you wish.
12. Dance or do some freeform movements. (Yogi Bhajan many times instructed us to dance at the end of a class. He said the structured Kundalini Yoga practice needs to be followed by freeform flowing movements.)

Cold Showers

Taking a cold shower in the morning before your sadhana is part of the recommended routine. The body however must be prepared so that it is not shocked by the cold water. There are several ways to do this; the choice is yours as long as you end your shower with water cold enough to increase the blood flow in the capillaries at the surface of the skin. Do not chill your internal organs.

Traditional instructions prescribe rubbing the body with oil and massaging briskly to warm up the body. Especially in dry climates, it is very healing to rub the body with almond, olive, sesame, or other medicinal oils. Brushing the body before the oil massage is also a powerful activator.

It is recommended to enter the cold water gradually, stimulating each limb with brisk massage as it enters the water. Remember the goal of the cold shower is to stimulate blood flow, not to shock your body or dramatically lower the temperature of your internal organs. Men should wear underwear to protect the sex organs from the cold. Women should wear shorts that cover the thighs. The calcium-magnesium balance in a woman's body is regulated in the thighs, and cold water on the thighs disturbs this balance.

Some people prefer to wash their body in warm water before the cold shower. If you choose this route, to get the effects of capillary blood flow, avoid water that is too hot and always end with cold water that is stimulating enough to wake you up and cleanse your aura. The longer the warm shower, the longer the cold shower must be to create the desired effects. As mentioned above, during her period, woman should avoid water that is too cold, but she can end her shower on the cool side to prevent feeling sluggish during the day.

What is cold? In Alaska and northern countries, cold can be about freezing, which is too cold. Add some hot in order to not shock your system. In warm climates, it is sometimes hard to find cold enough water to create the desired effect.

Also, your body type as set out in Ayurveda determines your body's sensitivity to cold showers. Vatta (air) types — delicate and super sensitive — need to avoid cold shocks to the system. Pitta (fire) and Kappa (earth and water) are more resilient and robust. Kappa types need the stimulation to get going.

Cleansing

The practice of Kundalini Yoga releases toxins into our bloodstream. We notice this especially when we begin our practice. This is good, because the accumulation of toxins causes disease. But sometimes we feel the effects as nausea or other signs of cleansing.

To accommodate the initial and ongoing release of toxins, we need to drink plenty of water, exercise, eat a cleansing diet, and possibly take cleansing herbs. Both fasting (there are many formulas) and taking a gradual, gentle approach to internal cleansing are recommended. We each have to find a formula that keeps our body active, nourished, and able to process cleansing. As we adopt a diet that eliminates toxic junk food and maintain a consistently healthy diet, the body naturally cleanses itself.

People think doing sadhana is a favor. Doing sadhana is relating to your soul. Soul has to be fed. Soul has to be enriched. Soul has to have prominence. Soul has to have overriding factors. Soul has to have executive order. Things have to be done for the soul.

7. Getting Started and Getting Results

Getting Started

It is recommended that total beginners pick one exercise, one meditation, or a kriya and do it any time of the day that is convenient. Repeat this exercise or choose another one for the next day. Experience how you feel. Do something and you will feel the effects. (To learn how I got started, see my introduction on page 5.)

Whatever exercise, meditation, or kriya you choose, do something every day, preferably before eating breakfast, turning on your computer or cell phone, and definitely before you leave the house.

Do Something Every Day!

During one class, I encouraged the students to practice for five minutes a day and then increase their time as they could. The next week a talented artist (who had never practiced outside of class before, had lots of emotional issues, and just couldn't get around to doing her artwork because of many excuses, including health problems) greeted me with her success. She had had the best week ever, felt very energized, completed lots of paintings, and felt great. I asked her what she had done. She said, "I set the kitchen timer for five minutes, ran into the bedroom, did five minutes of yoga, and stopped when the timer went off." She was delighted with her success and the immediate impact of her glorious five-minute sadhana. I was impressed too! Five minutes was life changing for her!

Program Yourself for Success

It is important to program yourself for success. If you can do five minutes a day, do five minutes *every* day. Then increase your time as you can. Do not start out with the false hope that you can do two hours or more, do it for one day, and then stop your practice because you feel discouraged by not being able to continue with a "perfect" sadhana.

Of course, the sooner you can establish a regular, committed practice, the better. Yes, even five minutes daily! Your progress is determined by your actual practice and your attention. The more you do what you do with feeling awareness, the more your inner guidance will direct your practice and your life.

How to Choose

The technology of Kundalini Yoga is so rich that beginners sometimes wonder what to choose first. In this manual, I share some basic kriyas and meditations that everyone can practice. If you are guided to a particular kriya or meditation, practice that.

It is a good idea to start with an exercise that will create immediate feel-good effects. One such exercise is the Four-Part Breath Meditation (described on page 141), which you can do for five minutes one or two times a day. You will immediately feel the energy and peace generated by this powerful pranayama exercise and want more. The Warm Up Series and Spinal Energy Series are also great beginner sets.

Choosing a Kriya and Meditation — Often Kundalini Yoga kriyas and meditations were taught separately, which means that unless specified you can mix and match the kriyas with the meditations. Your choice depends upon what you wish to work on.

Never Underestimate the Power of the Basics

The many techniques of Kundalini Yoga can be intimidating at first. However, you can avoid using that as an excuse for not getting started by keeping your practice simple. Here is a story to help you get started: One of Yogi Bhajan's first students recounted that he taught a class to beginners and told them to pick one exercise and make it their practice. Months later he was walking on the beach when he saw one of his former students with a radiant aura and huge smile. He asked him, "Wow, you look so bright and happy. What do you do?" The young man responded proudly, "I do Spinal Flex!" That was it! He did Spinal Flexes every day. So pick one (or more if you wish) and get started. Never underestimate the power of the basics of Kundalini Yoga! (Since I personally started doing Spinal Flex every day, I haven't had a lower backache!)

Getting Results

Kundalini Yoga is similar to learning to play a musical instrument, weight training, or any other sport or creative endeavor: you have to train to get results. The benefits that you receive depend upon (1) what you do, (2) how much you do, (3) your level of attention or inattention, and (4) your attitude, which can range from enjoyment to beating yourself up.

Repetition and Alternating Kriyas

Kriyas and meditations can be performed for many days in a row to fully generate and anchor in their effects. We can also vary our practice so that different areas are affected and pranic energy builds up through our whole system. Gradually, and in a matter of weeks or months, our body and mind go through a profound biological, physiological, and spiritual transformation, moving us toward overall electromagnetic balance.

How Many Days to Get a Result?

In the yogic tradition, meditations practiced for a certain number of days have a certain effect. Forty days is the minimum to break a habit and set the stage for an internal shift. A student asked me once, "40 days in a row?!" The whole class laughed. Yes, 40 days in a row! And if that seems like a long time, keep in mind that in the past, many spiritual masters have taken 40 *years* to achieve enlightenment. Most of those reading these words have probably done that path in other lifetimes. This lifetime, we are attempting to get quicker results!

In ancient times, a student came to a master for a meditation and then went away for years to practice and master the meditation. In our culture of quick fixes, we expect instantaneous results with little effort. When we practice with feeling awareness, and not just mechanically while we are thinking about something else, we achieve more favorable results.

Once you have established a program that works for you, continue practicing a kriya or meditation for at least 40 days.

The amount of time required is the amount of time that it takes to create a desired effect! Basically, keep going until the negative effects are corrected and you achieve a satisfactory shift in your life and in your consciousness. Maybe it takes more than 90 days, maybe 120, or 200, or 300, or 1,000 days. Although these timeframes are given (see below) and practicing for that many days certainly produces results, there is no absolute formula.

One student stopped doing Kundalini Yoga, claiming it didn't work because he wasn't prosperous after doing a prosperity meditation for 40 days. It is naive to think that bad habits and suboptimal attitudes that we have indulged in for many years (even lifetimes) are going to magically disappear in exactly 40 days. Witness what is changing in your psyche and in your life and be grateful.

Over time, the techniques given by Yogi Bhajan create powerful and profound results. Part of a daily practice includes monitoring the changes that you are undergoing. What is shifting? If you don't feel anything yet, you are not done yet. Keep going until you feel that the desired changes are encoded in your psyche.

The optimal time to begin a new set or meditation is on the *new moon*. Try it and witness for yourself that it is easier to maintain your practice for the number of days chosen.

Yogi Bhajan recommended doing a kriya or meditation every day in a row for the following number of days to achieve a specific level of results:

40 days breaks a habit.
90 days installs a new habit.
120 days encodes the habit.
1,000 days leads to mastery.

♥♥♥

Missing a Day

What happens if you miss a day in your 40-day program? This is not optimal, but it is not the end of the world. If this is your very first meditation or kriya, follow the general rule and start counting again from day one. Discipline and commitment are required for spiritual advancement. It takes time to change energetic patterns and habits and to install new ones. But missing a day does not discount the effect of the previous days. Keep going.

If you have been practicing daily for a year or so, perhaps for the one missed day, you may need to do an extra 7-10 days. It all depends. For example, if for some reason one day you can't practice your meditation for the full 31 minutes, do 5 minutes to sustain the effect. Basically keep going until the negative effects are corrected and you achieve the results that you are looking for.

Beginning and Advanced

Beginners sometimes ask if a particular mantra or kriya is appropriate for them. Kundalini Yoga doesn't classify mantras as beginning and advanced. However, there are basic kriyas and mantras that are recommended to practice as beginners (for example, the mantras SAT NAM and SA TA NA MA; see Kirtan Kriya on page 138). After you learn the basics, choose the mantra, meditation, and Kundalini Yoga kriya that fits your needs and goals. Practice it for 40, 90, 180, or 1,000 days, or until you feel you have achieved the results you desire.

In other words, begin your practice and over time you will achieve greater levels of inner peace, happiness, and self-esteem; expand your awareness; connect with deeper levels of who you are; and establish your relationship with your soul and universal forces. Practice, or sadhana, is an ongoing, evolutionary process. There is always more!

Commitment or Addiction?

A student once asked me, "I have been doing Kundalini Yoga for almost a year now. If I skip *one* day, I feel empty, unfulfilled, and unsatisfied. If it's not a reliance on (an addiction to) Kundalini Yoga, then what is it?"

My answer: A connection to your higher self is not an addiction. Kundalini Yoga is a technology to deliver you to your true self. You are finding that you are more comfortable feeling connected to your soul and the Infinite within than to the emptiness of your limited ego. Your practice of Kundalini Yoga is helping you achieve your goal of contacting that part of yourself that can guide you to inner peace and happiness. You have reached the level of practice where you are committed to training yourself to rely on your soul and be guided by your heart. This is great progress for which you can be most grateful. (See the discussion on addictions in Part III.)

What Is the Kundalini?

Kundalini is the energy of our soul.

Kundalini is the energy of consciousness.
Kundalini is the awareness of our higher self.
Kundalini is our emanation of Infinity.
Kundalini is the energy of the cosmos within each individual.

Kundalini is our creative energy.

Kundalini is imagined as a coiled serpent lying asleep at the base of our spine.
Kundalini is the dormant energy within us that expands our awareness.
Kundalini is the greatness of which we are each capable.

When we tap our Kundalini, what do we become aware of?

We become aware of our creative capacities and our radiant caliber.
We become aware of our personal relationship with Infinity.
Kundalini makes it possible for us as humans with finite personalities to relate to
our soul identity.

What makes it possible to experience Kundalini energy?

When the glandular system is activated and the nervous system is strong
the energies of the two systems combine to create
a movement or flow in the spinal fluid
a sensitivity in the nerve endings.
The entire brain receives signals and integrates them.

What is the result?

A new clarity expands our perceptual awareness.
We understand the effect and impact of an action before we take it.
We are at choice whether to act or not to act.
Awareness brings choice.
Choice brings freedom.

Is Kundalini energy necessary?

We cannot live without a constant flow of Kundalini energy.
The difference is the amount of the flow.
When there is an abundant flow of Kundalini
our mind awakens from its long nap
we stop living in imaginary realities
we become committed to our purpose and our service
we enjoy the abundant pleasures of life.

Part II: Basic Techniques

8. The Locks/Bhandas

The locks, or bhandas, are delicate alignments of the muscles along the spine and the subtle positioning of the body and spine that help facilitate the easy flow of energy up and down the spine. The light application of locks/bhandas also helps us maintain proper posture.

- **Root lock** (mul bhand), involving the first three chakras, creates a base, grounding, and a foundation.
- **Diaphragm lock** (uddyana bhand) keeps us from slumping in the middle of our body and opens our heart.
- **Neck lock** (jalandara bhand) also facilitates good posture, opens our heart, positions our head on our spine so that our shoulders do not have to support the weight of our head, and creates the space for the energy to flow between the body and the head.
- **Mahabhand** is the simultaneous application of all three locks.

As you apply each lock, notice the position and sensations in your spine. Application of the locks with various levels of intensity (lighter and deeper) are an integral aspect of Kundalini Yoga and are almost always used in some form (1) during the exercises, (2) after an exercise to move the energy up the spine, (3) during pranayama, and (4) during meditation to maintain the flow of energy in the spine.

How to Apply the Locks/Bhandas

Root lock involves activating the energies at the root, sex, and navel chakras. The respective chakras are stimulated by first pulling the muscles at the base of the spine, anus, and perineum. Second, pulling the muscles at the sex organ. For men, this involves the muscles in the penis that are used to stop urination. In women, this involves the vaginal muscles. And third, pulling the navel in and slightly up toward the spine. These are delicate contractions, not intense constrictions. Their purpose is to open and direct, not restrict, the flow of energy.

Practice pulling and releasing each muscle group to connect with and develop these muscles. Because these muscles are connected, you will find that applying the lock in one area engages the muscles in the other areas. They all work together.

Root lock combines the energies of the first three chakras, causing their energies to interact in a way that releases the Kundalini.

1. Root lock at the **first chakra** connects us to feeling sensitivity in our body and to Mother Earth energy.

2. Root lock at the **second chakra** uses the ojas, or charge from the sexual energy, to unleash our creative energy, feed the brain, and stimulate the activation of the Kundalini.
3. By bringing 72,000 nerve endings together, root lock at the **navel** acts as a powerful centering mechanism. As the nerves are aligned, we build a strong electrical charge or fire/tappa that descends to activate the Kundalini.

A light root lock is applied while doing many Kundalini Yoga exercises. We "establish our root" (1) to contain our energy in our body and (2) to create an internal structure to "hold" the body while performing various exercises.

Diaphragm lock (uddyana bhand) keeps us from slumping in the middle of our body and opens the heart. Full diaphragm lock is done by pulling up and in on the diaphragm during the suspended exhale. However, we always keep the diaphragm extended upward and add this extension on the supended inhale as well.

Neck lock (jalandara bhand) is a subtle positioning of the head to (1) open the flow of energy between the body and the head; (2) correct slumped posture; (3) open the throat chakra by relaxing the shoulders, mouth, tongue, and face; and (4) open the heart.

To perform neck lock,

- First pull up on the diaphragm to correct a slumping posture.
- Pull your head up from the back of the neck. The head will go back slightly.
- The chin comes straight back and very slightly down.
- The upper vertebra (axis/atlas) are elongated up and back.
- Feel how the position of the neck shifts your posture, elongates your spine, and opens the chest.
- Feel an opening and release of "holding" in the throat/neck area.

The neck lock is applied in conjunction with the other locks while suspending the breath and is lightly used during most exercises and meditations. When the directions say "Sit with a straight spine," pull up on the diaphragm to ensure an open-hearted posture, and position your head on your spine so that your shoulders are not slumped forward.

Mahabhand

Mahabhand is the term used when we apply all the locks — root, diaphragm, and neck — simultaneously. At the end of an exercise, it is assumed that we (or the teacher says) "apply the locks." This indicates that we are to align the spine and direct the energy upward to the third eye, where we maintain our mental focus.

Eye Focus

The third eye is located in the center of the forehead slightly above the eyebrows. Focusing at the third eye to activate the sixth chakra awakens our neutral mind and activates the capacity of our mind to stay centered and present. We can get ungrounded and unfocused if we "escape" out the top of our head.

However, sometimes an exercise, such as Sat Kriya, does call for moving the energy out the top of the head. To move the energy up to the crown, we focus the eyes up to the top of the head and press the tongue to the roof of the mouth.

The directions in many meditations tell us to focus the eyes at the tip of the nose with the eyes about nine-tenths closed or one-tenth open. This is a very soft gaze. The eyes focused (gazing softly) at the tip of the nose creates a sensation or pressure at the third eye, making it easier to bring our mental focus to that point. Both the pineal and the pituitary glands are stimulated by this eye posture, which stabilizes and calms the mind and directs our attention to the stillness within. It also has the effect of breaking old habits and creating new ones.

There are several ways to facilitate looking at the tip of the nose. Here are two: (1) Bring your forefinger in front of your face and look at it. Keep looking at the forefinger as you slowly bring the forefinger toward the tip of the nose. (2) Extend the arms out to your sides parallel to the ground, palms up. Do Breath of Fire for 1-3 minutes. This exercise balances the right and left hemispheres of the brain, which makes it easier to maintain the focus of the two eyes. This balancing of the brain's hemispheres also awakens the neutral mind. It is a great warm up to do before any kriya or meditation.

Posture and an Open Heart

As we cultivate awareness of the spine, head, and root, we can make subtle adjustments to keep our heart open. We can then easily observe how good posture supports an open heart. Here are some tips on how to improve your posture and open your heart.

Lotus Pose

Lotus Pose is ideal for meditation because it positions the spine with the chest forward so the energy flows naturally up and down the spine. Most of us sit in Easy Pose or half Lotus because we can't get into full Lotus, or if we can, we can't maintain it comfortably for very long. But if we can get into Lotus Pose even briefly, we can feel how it aligns our spine.

The basic problem with Easy Pose is that we have a tendency to slump. When the spine is out of alignment, the natural flow of the Kundalini is impeded. A simple solution is to prop the buttocks up with a firm cushion ("lotus pillow") in a way that prevents the spine from slumping and the chest from caving in.

Meditation benches are another alternative, but the bench must fit the student. Once I sat on a computer bench that sent me into immediate meditation. I experienced that when the spine is correctly aligned, deep meditation is greatly facilitated.

Computer Pose and Chin Lock

Most of us are so mental that our head protrudes out in front of our body and leads us around when we walk. When our head is not positioned correctly above the spine, we slump and our heart closes. Poor posture, neck, and back problems result. Many people sit in "computer pose" most of the day — sticking their neck out and head forward. The slumped spine and caved-in chest syndrome are endemic. We can move from computer pose to an expanded chest simply by pulling our head back slightly, pulling up on our spine from the back of our neck, and raising our diaphragm. Our spine straightens and our heart opens.

Our head is in the right position when our chest expands, our shoulders relax, and we smile! When the head protrudes forward, the upper back and shoulder muscles tighten to support the weight of the head. We look serious and don't smile. To cultivate an aligned posture habit, practice moving the head forward and then back and up into alignment. Take time (at least a couple of breaths after the movement) to actually let your shoulders and upper back muscles relax when the head feels like it is floating above the spine. These muscles aren't accustomed to relaxing. They need sensitivity training to create a new habit.

Posture Starts in the Feet

The picture above of a woman in high heels hunched over a computer desk illustrates a very important fact about posture. Wearing high-heeled shoes shortens the hamstring muscles in the back of the calves. Short hamstring muscles pull on the thigh muscles and the hips. As the hips adjust to compensate, our posture collapses. Men are fortunate that most of their footwear supports good posture, though they still often have tight hamstring muscles that undermine good posture. Delicate stretching can gradually elongate and loosen up the hamstrings. Weight training needs to be balanced with stretching that keeps the blood flowing in the muscles. Stagnant blood hardens the muscles and sabotages flexibility.

Upper Back Muscles Support an Open Heart

The upper back muscles need to both learn to relax and be strengthened to support an open heart. While doing heart-opening exercises (like Spinal Twists — inhaling left and exhaling right with the arms up or on the shoulders), use the muscles in the back opposite the heart to press the shoulder blades together. Before initiating these movements, press the shoulder blades together to get in touch with the muscles that make this possible. This is an internal isometric movement. You can feel how these muscles support opening the heart as they push the chest forward from behind. These subtle movements, done gently and consciously, build muscle tone, train the muscles to relax, and release tension.

Spinal Flexes on the knees are perfect for exercising these muscles. Use the movement of the arms on the inhale to press the shoulder blades together and the chest out. Be aware of the sensations in your spine between the shoulder blades to cultivate the awareness that the heart center includes the back of the body as well as the front of the body and everything in between.

Elongate and Relax Pectoral Muscles in Front of Body

To support an open heart and good posture, the pectoral muscles in the front upper chest should be long and relaxed. Slumped posture causes the pectorals to contract and tense up. It is important to develop an awareness of our pectoral muscles.

Spinal Flexes in Easy Pose with the hands on the ankles or on the knees elongate the pectorals. Pay attention to lengthening the pectorals while doing these Spinal Flexes. Create more of a stretch by slightly pulling the head up and back from the neck during the stretch up as you gently pull up on the ankles or the knees.

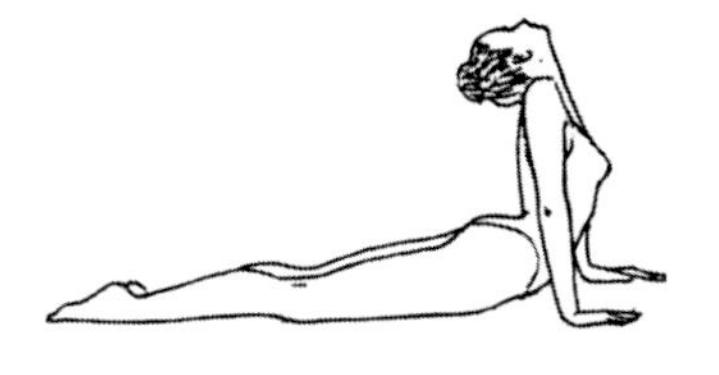

We also pay attention to lengthen the pectorals in Cobra Pose and other exercises where we arch backwards. Then we can stretch the upper spine and avoid arching only in our lower back. However, we avoid arching the head back in a way that compresses the vertebrae in the neck. The spine should be pulled up from the neck, which remains in a straight line with the spine (not crushed back).

During our daily life, we can adjust our posture by using the upper body muscles in the front and back of our body in the following manner:

1. Pulling up on our diaphragm and raising our chest muscles
2. Elongating our spine by pulling up and back from the back of our neck

Using these two different sets of muscles helps strengthen and relax both sets.

Leg Stretches with an Open Heart and Legs Straight

Kundalini postures, including leg stretches, should be done with an open chest. Except for very flexible bodies, this normally requires curving the back, closing the heart, and bending the knee. Keeping the knee straight and foot flat helps lengthen the hamstring muscles, which when short, pull on the hips and back muscles, contributing to poor posture.

In leg stretches, the bend should be from the hips, lengthening the spine and aiming the chest toward the thighs. However far you can go, maintain the integrity of the spine and an expanded chest to receive the benefits of the posture. For those who cannot reach their toes, avoid bending your knees to compensate, and use straps to help you achieve your maximum stretch. Be very gentle to protect delicate muscles at the small of the back.

Create a Foundation in the Lower Chakras

One of the reasons why we are so mentally preoccupied is that we aren't connected to our lower chakras and Mother Earth. And thus we are not consciously present to our feelings in our body. The more we cultivate awareness and centered core power in our navel charka and abdominal/pelvic area, the more we create a foundation to support an open heart. It is important to monitor how the concentration of our energy shifts as we develop our core. After lower charka exercises, we become less mental and top heavy. We think less and feel more.

Tuck the Tailbone — Establish Your Root

Pulling our navel in and up creates a slight tucking of our tailbone. This aligns the lower spine and pulls our energy downward. The pulling of the anus muscles and inward pull of the navel center in root lock create an inner foundation in our lower chakras. *This is called establishing our root.* It is important to take the time to gently work with the muscles and energy in the pelvis and abdomen and to experience how they participate in aligning the spine.

These lower adjustments protect the delicate back muscles by promoting the use of other muscles to maintain correct posture. To establish our central core, it is also very important to strengthen the smaller abdominal muscles that rest on top of the larger psoas muscles.

Tucking the tailbone, root lock, and neck lock work together to elongate the spine. Cultivate awareness of the connection between the root and the neck and experience how these delicate movements work together to align the spine, create relaxed posture, and open the heart.

Spinal Twists

As mentioned above, Kundalini Yoga works with angles. The different variations of Spinal Twist are good examples of where the angle is important and should be maintained while performing the twisting motion. First, establish the arm position parallel to the ground. Lock in this position and hold it while turning left and right. Move the body as a unit. The arms should not bob around. The head moves to each side with the movement.

Shoulder Shrugs and Neck Rolls

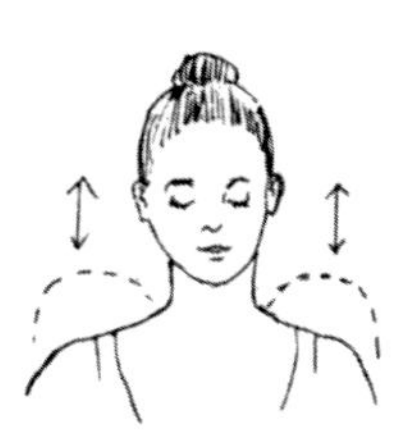

Shoulder Shrugs (slowly inhaling as shoulders go up and exhaling down) loosen a lot of upper body muscles, both front and back. Before doing this exercise, notice any tendency to keep the shoulders tense. After the exercise, relax the shoulders and feel the shoulder blades drop. Notice that when your shoulders relax, the neck and face begin to relax too.

You need to feel that your neck is relaxed and floating on the top of your spine before doing neck rolls. It is important to do neck rolls very slowly. Start with slow small circles. Only increase the movement if it feels comfortable. Any movements that are painful are counterproductive. Never go back too far, as it can crunch the vertebrae. Relaxed and open is the goal, and this can be achieved with small, gentle movements.

Eye Exercises

Doing eye exercises is an effective way to relax the neck and shoulder muscles and to facilitate neck rolls. Do neck rolls before and after eye exercises and notice the difference. Eye exercises also have the effect of opening up other parts of the body so that performing a posture is easier. Try doing Cobra Pose before and after doing eye exercises.

Eye Exercises with the Eyes Closed

Any sequence is fine, but here is a complete sequence:

- Look up, down, to the right, to the left, 10 o'clock to 4 o'clock, 11 to 5, 1 to 7, 2 to 8.
- Make counterclockwise circles and then clockwise.
- Make figure eights up and down, right to left, 10 o'clock to 4 o'clock, 11 to 5, 1 to 7, 2 to 8.
- Switch directions of figure eights.

Between Exercises and Ending Your Session with Grounding

Between exercises, adjust the neck and the root, and with your breath, relax and let go. During the passive period, keep your focus on the sensations in your body and spine and monitor how letting go can shift both your posture and the flow of energy. As you focus on your spine, establish it as a stable support for correct and relaxed posture.

At the end of your practice, stand up and walk around the room, noticing your posture and how the lengthening and relaxing of the pectorals, the position of your head, and opening of the heart make it possible to stand and walk taller. Feel your feet connect with Mother Earth. You are here now ready to participate in life and to enjoy another great day!

9. Pranayama

Pranayama, or breathing techniques, is fundamental to Kundalini Yoga and Meditation. Powerful breathing patterns significantly enhance the effects of the exercises and meditations. Pranayama oxygenates the entire body, clearing the mind, strengthening the nervous system, balancing the two hemispheres of the brain, cleaning the aura, detoxifying the body, improving digestion, and releasing fears, insecurity, irritability, depression, and other fear-based blocks.

Pranayama exercises also balance prana and apana. *Prana* is the basic life force that animates our being. *Apana* is the energy that makes elimination possible. When the apana in the lower chakras mixes with prana (by applying the locks while suspending the breath), heat (referred to as tappa) is generated, which raises the Kundalini up the spine through the chakras.

Mind and Breath

Pranayama helps us cultivate breath awareness and integrate conscious breathing into our daily life and yogic practice.

The breath and our state of mind are intricately linked. We can control our mind by controlling our breath. Most of us breathe very shallow breaths and take 15 or more breaths per minute. Breathing more than 10 breaths per minute creates a state of stress. People who suffer from panic attacks not only breathe quickly and shallowly, they also often breathe through their mouths.

To create a state of peace and relaxation, we must breathe fewer than 10 breaths per minute. Breathing four or fewer breaths per minute induces a state of meditation. We must also inhale and exhale through the nose.

Whenever you want to calm down, paying attention to your breath is the first step. Notice if you are inhaling and exhaling through your mouth or nose. Notice where you are breathing in your body. How far down do you breathe? Do you breathe from your belly, chest, or neck? How many times do you breathe per minute? Time yourself.

Basic Yogic Breathing

It is very important to learn to do the breathing properly in Kundalini Yoga exercises and meditations. The basic breaths described below are

- Long deep breathing
- Suspending the breath
- Breath of Fire
- Right, left, and alternate nostril breathing

- Segmented breath
- Passive awareness breathing
- One-minute breath

These breathing techniques are used in conjunction with specific postures and movements to create powerful effects.

Long Deep Breathing

Posture Improves Breathing Capacity

To facilitate the free flow of our breath and pranic energy, we must keep our spine stretched upward. There are three stretch zones in our spine that correspond to the three sets of muscles that move on our inhale and exhale. Aligning and stretching the spine in these three zones facilitates deep breathing.

1. ***From the sit bones to the bottom of the ribs***
   Slightly pull your navel toward your spine to tilt your pelvis forward. Notice that instead of leaning forward, your posture will become more upright. You will be sitting on your sit bones, which connect you more solidly with the floor and facilitate grounding with the Earth. This position frees the belly muscles, which are able to relax and made available for long deep breathing.

2. ***Bottom of ribcage to top of rib cage***
   The muscles that surround the ribcage must be developed and strengthened to breathe long and deep. Lifting the solar plexus expands the chest and makes it easier to engage the major muscles of the diaphragm.

3. ***From upper rib to base of skull*** (where the vertebra sticks out)
   The smaller muscles above the diaphragm are used to extend the breath to its maximum inhale.

Exhalation and Inhalation

Some people prematurely cut off their exhalation and then initiate their inhalation with the use of the small respiratory muscles in the upper chest instead of using the muscles in the diaphragm. They think they have to emphasize the inhale to get enough air. However, a deep inhalation is dependent upon a full exhalation. Before your practice, observe your breath and notice the length of both your inhale and exhale. Some people emphasize the inhale and some emphasize the exhale.

Simple Exercise

A simple exercise to increase your exhalation is to breathe through a straw. When you breathe through a straw, it takes longer to exhale and thus trains your body to exhale using the diaphragm. Blowing through a musical instrument and chanting a long tone also forces you to use your diaphragm to extend the sound being produced on your exhale. Practice extending a note as long as you can by engaging your diaphragm.

Results of Diaphragm Breathing

With practice (1) both your inhalations and exhalations will significantly lengthen, (2) your diaphragm will become stronger, and (3) your diaphragm will automatically engage to produce your inhale and exhale. Ultimately, your breathing mechanism will be activated and will engage in long, smooth inhales and exhales. This practice is also a great way to improve your vocal capacity.

Count Your Breaths

Before long deep breathing exercises, count the number of breaths that your body is breathing per minute.

As you practice extending both your inhale and your exhale by using your diaphragm to breathe long and deep, you will notice that you are breathing four, three, and even two breaths per minute. As your breath becomes deeper and slower, notice where your mind is. Yogis say that breathing fewer than four breaths per minute awakens the meditative, creative mind. This is where you enter the "zone" and operate from a very different place than your "thinking" mind. You enter your intuitive, neutral mind.

Relax, Release Tension in Your Body

Be sure to monitor the stress/relaxation state of your body. After the deep inhale, take a moment to make sure you relax your shoulders, face, neck, and chest. Your exhale will of course have to be controlled to progressively extend it, but your body doesn't and shouldn't be tight. Releasing tension adds to your enjoyment and to the quality and projection of your voice.

Long Deep Diaphragm Breathing and Breath Awareness Exercise

While consciously practicing long deep breathing, there are several things to be aware of:

- Keep your spine stretched by keeping the diaphragm at the solar plexus pulled up. Make sure that your head is positioned so that your chest comes forward. Stretch the neck upward and back a bit and slightly tuck the chin. You will feel the correct position when your shoulders move back and down and relax.
- Check to make sure that your chest cavity and abdomen *expand* like a balloon *on the inhale* and *contract on the exhale*. Some people actually have this reversed.
- Begin with an extended exhale to clear your lungs of old air and to maximize the space available to receive your inhale. Your exhale determines how much you can inhale.

- Inhale deeply down to the bottom of the lungs by allowing the lower part of the diaphragm to expand downward and out against the abdomen. The back should expand behind the solar plexus area, which feeds the kidneys with prana. Put your hands on your back to feel the expansion. When you are lying on your back, your back will move toward the floor.
- Feel the breath infuse your body with pranic energy as your lungs expand on the inhalation. Increase your lung capacity by expanding a little more on each inhale and contracting a little more on each exhale.

Results
With each breath, more and more prana moves through and accumulates in the body. You will feel more and more aliveness, vitality, and radiance throughout your body, as well as in your aura.

As you continue deep diaphragm breathing, you will notice an awakening of the neutral mind, increased awareness, and a sense of being open, clear, light, and expansive.

Suspending the Breath

When we say "hold the breath" in Kundalini Yoga, we really mean suspend the breath, which can be done either after a deep inhalation or after the exhalation. As a default instruction after most exercises, we suspend the breath on both the inhale and exhale. The suspended inhale balances prana. The suspended exhale balances apana. Together prana and apana are mixed and play a part in activating the Kundalini. Sometimes the directions say to apply several suspended breaths at the end of an exercise.

Pranayama and suspending the breath are both energizing and relaxing. *Suspending the breath on the inhale* affects the sympathetic nervous system, which is activating and stimulating, puts the body on alert mode, and can raise our blood pressure temporarily.

Suspending the breath on the exhale affects the parasympathetic nervous system, which is relaxing, puts the body on "let go" mode, and can lower the blood pressure temporarily.

In general, pranayama balances our blood pressure, and many people have experienced that they achieve a necessary lowering of blood pressure.

How to Suspend the Breath on the Inhale and Mahabhand

- Draw in air with an initial long inhalation followed by shorter "sniffs" at the end to complete the inhale. You can feel the moment when the clavicles lock in. There is no more space to inhale.
- Once the inhale is complete, it is important to *relax* the whole body into the state of suspension. The body has the tendency to become tense and the shoulders go up while

completing the inhale. Make sure the shoulders relax down. When the body is relaxed, we are able to hold the breath in longer.

- While suspending the inhaled breath, gently and consciously apply the locks. Use the neck lock to keep the spine stretched up. Use root lock to direct the Kundalini energy up the spine. At the diaphragm, focus on lifting the solar plexus to open the space in this area.

How to Suspend the Breath on the Exhale and Mahabhand

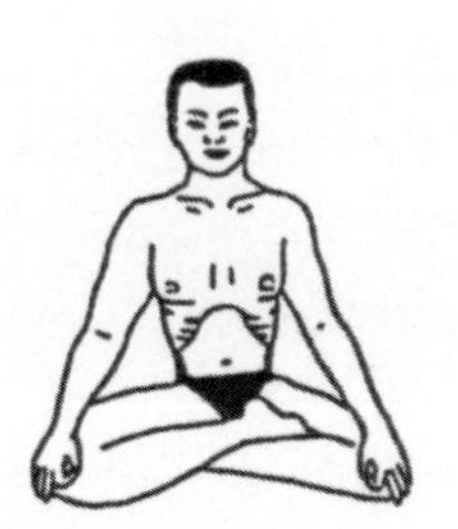

- Exhale with a long exhale followed by shorter exhales. However, do not force all the air out of your lungs. If we expel all the air, the body will gasp for air.
- Near the end of the exhale, begin pulling in the navel and applying the root lock. This will hold a small amount of air in the lungs, making it possible to sustain the exhale. As you exhale, squeeze the breath out from the top of the lungs downward until you feel the sides coming in toward the navel, and the area below the navel and diaphragm contracting upward.

It is important to relax the whole body into the state of suspension, which makes it possible to hold out the breath longer. Suspending the breath after the exhale is powerful because it is now easier to pull the diaphragm up. As you relax into the suspension, further contract the diaphragm muscles and draw them inward and upward toward the heart. Feel the fire at the navel center move up to the heart.

Experiences While Suspending the Breath

As you hold and increase the pressure of the diaphragm lock and the root lock,

- Allow the pranic pressure and heat to rise through the spinal cord to the third eye.
- Pay attention at the pranic center just below the sternum. As the pranic center opens, you can feel warm pulsing sensations at your heart center.
- Let your inner space expand to include your mind, heart, and body. Your awareness will be drawn inward to your still, neutral space.
- Deeply listen! Feel! Pay attention! This is a sacred moment, which is free of thoughts; you can access your soul and the Infinite.

After releasing the suspension, relax into the flow of your breath.

Effects of Suspending the Breath

When suspension of the breath is done properly and deeply while applying the locks

- The mixing of prana and apana activates the Kundalini, producing heat in the spine.

- The pranic pressure allows the heat/Kundalini to rise up the spine, filling the body with radiance and the mind with consciousness.
- The pranic energy that comes from changing the ratio of carbon dioxide to oxygen in the bloodstream is increased, releasing tension in the brain and body.
- The mind is drawn inward and bows as it joins as one with the heart.

Imprint a Divine Message and Clear the Subconscious

It is powerful (and recommended) to mentally chant a mantra of your choice while suspending your breath. The mantra makes it easier to hold your breath in or out. The vibration and message of the sacred mantras work to clear subconscious programming, imprint a divine affirmation in your psyche, and elevate your consciousness. There are many Kundalini meditations that include mentally chanting a divine mantra on the suspended breath. More on that in the next chapter.

Breath of Fire

Breath of Fire is key to the practice of Kundalini Yoga. Breath of Fire (1) helps oxygenate the blood, (2) energizes and nurtures all the body's systems, (3) aligns the navel chakra, (4) activates our capacity to focus and be centered in our body, and (5) creates the heat necessary to stimulate the awakening of the Kundalini.

How to Do Breath of Fire Correctly

- Pull the navel toward the spine on the exhale. The navel relaxes and goes back out on the inhale. This should be done as a rhythmic pumping.
- Focus on the short exhales. *Only the exhale is active.* The inhale happens automatically.
- Breath of Fire is a light, not a heavy, breath. Make sure the movement at the navel is staccato, relaxed, and rhythmic.
- *Do not* consciously engage the abdominal muscles. The breath will be too slow and get even slower and heavier.
- Do not tense or use the muscles of the chest, shoulders, or face. The muscles of the shoulders, chest, and ribcage remain relaxed.
- Feel the movement of air deep in the lungs and in the chest area.

Tips for Learning Breath of Fire

- Start with long deep breathing to become aware of your abdominal and diaphragm muscles and your breathing mechanism.
- Panting with your mouth open is a helpful exercise for getting in touch with using the muscles of the navel and diaphragm to do quick rhythmic breathing.

- When learning Breath of Fire, practice the breath a short time (even a few seconds) and then stop. When the breath starts to feel heavy or not right, stop. Allow your breath to relax before recommencing. It often takes some time to get it right, so don't force it. Just practice, stop, and start again. It may even take a few days until you get into the light rhythm. You will know when you get it because you will be able to continue for longer times without slowing down or building up tension.

Breath of Fire Done Incorrectly

A common mistake is to actively inhale as well as exhale. This slows down the breath. Only the exhale is active. The inhale is the same length as the exhale, but we allow it to happen instead of making it happen.

When Breath of Fire is done incorrectly, the abdominal, side back, ribcage, and shoulder muscles have a tendency to become tense instead of being completely relaxed. After a minute or two, the tensing begins to become tedious and sporadic, and the breath loses its rhythm. The result is that the energy from the breath does not flow to the areas under pressure from the exercise. Instead, the breath goes mostly to the external muscles of the abdomen, side back, ribs, and shoulders. We even use the muscles of our face, which, when under the strain of breathing improperly, becomes somewhat contorted.

Hatha Yoga Breathing Compared to Breath of Fire

Breath of Fire is similar to Agni Prasana in Hatha Yoga. Breath of Fire is *not* Kapalabhati or Bhastrika as practiced in Hatha Yoga. These breaths are powerful pranayamas, but they differ in the following ways:

Kapalabhati — More Exhale Than Inhale

In Kapalabhati breath, the emphasis and effort is only on the exhale. No effort is made to breathe in, although some inhale happens automatically. In Kapalabhati, the navel is forced in on the exhale, and the air forced/squeezed out. More air is thus expelled than inhaled.

Length

The exhale in Kapalabhati is performed once per second, or 60 times per minute, which is slower than Breath of Fire, which is 2-3 times per second. Because we exhale more than we inhale, Kapalabhati breath is difficult to maintain for more than a few minutes at a time.

Cleansing

Kapalabhati breath focuses more on cleansing and elimination. This breath releases physical impurities, disease, and mental and emotional negativity.

Bhastricka

In Bhastricka breath, both the inhale and exhale are forceful. The duration of both the inhale and exhale is 2½ seconds each, or 12 times per minute. This breath is powerful, but it is also difficult to maintain for more than a few minutes at a time.

Right, Left, and Alternate Nostril Breathing

Left Nostril Breathing

Left nostril breathing activates lunar energy and the qualities of patience and letting go. Do left nostril breathing to relax, calm the mind, and cool the nerves. It is soothing to do left nostril breathing any time you wish to relax and before going to bed.

How to Do Left Nostril Breathing
Block the right nostril with the right thumb and inhale and exhale through the left nostril only, using long deep breathing unless specified differently in a kriya.

Right Nostril Breathing

Right nostril breathing energizes and alleviates irritated, depressed, or unbalanced mental and emotional states. It activates solar energy and the qualities of strong will, perseverance, motivation, and the ability to take action and keep up. If you are tired, falling asleep, and need more energy, breathe through the right nostril.

How to Do Right Nostril Breathing
Block the left nostril with the left thumb and inhale and exhale long and deeply through the right nostril only. Or do Breath of Fire through the right nostril for a quick boost of energy.

Alternate Nostril Breathing

The different techniques of alternate nostril breathing create a balanced state that is both relaxed and energizing. There are many variations of alternate nostril breathing, blocking alternate nostrils. The most common pattern is

Inhale left
Exhale right, Inhale right
Exhale left, Inhale left
Exhale right, Inhale right
Exhale left

The simple formula is exhale and inhale through one nostril and then switch and exhale and inhale through the other nostril.

Remember, the sides of the body expand on the inhale. The shoulders stay relaxed and do not move up and down.

I originally learned alternate nostril breathing from my mother, who learned it during her discovery of Hatha Yoga. I remember my mother always having sinus issues. She had little respiratory inhalers in every room of the house. During one visit home, I noticed the absence of these inhalers and that my mother didn't have any more sinus problems. I asked her what had happened? She said she eliminated her sinus issues by doing alternate nostril breathing. I have offered this remedy to others, who always reported success.

Segmented Breath

Segmented breath divides each inhalation and exhalation into several equal parts. Instead of inhaling or exhaling in one long stroke, we inhale or exhale in 2, 4, 8, 12, or 16 equal segments. The sum of the segments equals a complete inhale or exhale.

There is a slight or momentary pause between each segment, which maintains the rhythmic breathing pattern. The same amount of air is received on each stroke and takes the same amount of time, creating a rhythm.

Although this is a conscious and not a natural breathing pattern, when it is light and rhythmic, it feels very natural and becomes automatic. Segmented breath is easy to coordinate with walking, inhaling four sniffs for four steps and exhaling four sniffs for four steps.

Passive Awareness Breathing

Being able to be with our breath and simply allowing our pranic body to breathe is as important as active pranayama exercises. We practice different breathing patterns so that we can strengthen and liberate our pranic body to breathe freely and deeply. Simply allowing and relaxing into the flow of our breath is a deep meditation on the flow of our soul.

After all pranayama, mantra, and physical exercises, take a few minutes to sit quietly and be with your breath as it moves through your body. Be with your breath in your body exactly the way it is, without controlling or altering it in any way. Focus totally on the rhythm and sensations of your breath in your body. Feel the wave of your breath in your chest and heart.

Don't be judgmental. Be compassionate. Being kind and compassionate brings all the goodness of the world to you.

One-Minute Breath

Yogi Bhajan recommended that everyone perfect the one-minute breath. Although this is not a beginning breath and is a more advanced form of breath control, everyone can prepare himself or herself to master this breath. The instructions are

1. With the eyes closed, inhale for 20 seconds.
2. Hold (suspend the breath) for 20 seconds.
3. Exhale for 20 seconds.

Someone with a big lung capacity can do this fairly easily. And then there are the rest of us who must develop our lung capacity, which can take a long time. The instructions above for long deep breathing and suspending the breath will help you cultivate this breath.

Obviously we have to master a very slow regulated long deep breath. We may need to add a few short sniffs to elongate the inhale. Be sure to relax and release tension while suspending the breath. Do not let any air seep out.

Also, don't try to do this breath without first preparing with long deep breathing and Breath of Fire. You will have more success at the end of your Kundalini Yoga practice when your body and breath have been warmed up.

A good way to practice this breath is to count with a mantra to avoid the stress and distraction of looking at the seconds of a clock. For example, the slow mental repetition of SA TA NA MA can take 4-5 seconds. Time yourself to monitor 1, 2, and 3 repetitions. Begin with 1 or 2 repetitions for all 3 segments and increase gradually. Each segment must be the same length. One or two segments might be easier, but that doesn't give one license to cheat on the other segment. You can choose any mantra that helps you keep time.

Start out with 3-5 minutes and work up to 11. Relax afterwards and allow the integration.

You live by the breath. You are born by the breath, and you die when the breath leaves you. The focal point of your being is the breath of life. Therefore, you must sit for your sake and meditate on your breath doing the One-Minute Breath for at least three minutes. When you establish the grounds, then you can establish the mantra. If you are a Jew, the sound is "Ya." If you are a Christian, the sound is "Ha." If you are a Muslim, the sound is "La." If you are a Hindu, the sound is "Ra." If you are a Sikh, the sound is "Sa." Choose it from your belief. With the eyes closed, inhale 20 seconds, hold 20 seconds, exhale 20 seconds.

Pay Attention to the Energetic Effects

During and after all pranayama exercises

- Feel the delicate pranic aliveness and increase of voltage, energy, lightness, and radiance throughout your body.
- Pay attention to different parts of your body (abdomen, sides, legs, lower spine, middle and upper parts of the back, solar plexus and chest, the shoulders, neck and throat, facial muscles, lips, jaw, eyes, and forehead), breathing into and relaxing each and every area.
- Use awareness to allow the energy being generated during an exercise to go to the actual areas being stimulated by the posture or movement.
- With awareness feel the sensations in your body and notice where there is tension, stress, or numbness. Release and relax these areas by allowing what you are feeling.

A LIBERATED PERSON is always a happy person. He does not lack in any material comfort. He does not know any power on earth which can insult him. He lives in grace in this world, and when he leaves the body, he is respected for generations to follow. Everyone can be like that. Yesterday's sinner can be a saint this minute! The only thing required is a decision. "Am I to guard my future and choose to be a liberated person or am I to block my future and be by the material-physical aspect of the world?"

1969

10. Mantras — Tuning In and Meditation

Mantra means the projection of the mind. Mantras use universal sound currents to rearrange the habit patterns of the mind. They do so by accessing the part of the mind that regulates habits. The sounds erase patterns that vibrate at lower frequencies or do not resonate with the Truth or our true essence. They establish new habits by replacing the old frequency with the higher frequency of the Truth.

Chanting mantras (1) brings coherency and clarity to our mental, physical, and emotional energy; (2) breaks down subtle blockages of energy flow; (3) creates a resonance between our mind and body and higher vibrations; (4) clears lower vibrations and releases negative subconscious programming; and (5) stimulates our glands to secrete, which helps activate and balance our chakras.

When we attach a mantra to our breath while doing the exercises and follow a kriya with a mantra meditation, the energetic frequency and radiance throughout our body, mind, and aura significantly increase.

The mantra sounds (whether chanted silently or out loud) further integrate the energy that has been systematically unleashed from each exercise, supporting and sustaining the increased build up of prana. The effect is similar to playing an electric guitar versus playing an accoustic guitar — the reverberation increases with the amplification of the voltage.

Tuning In Mantra — Invocation/Dedication

We always begin our Kundalini Yoga practice by chanting the Adi Mantra:

ONG NAMO GURU DEV (Day) NAMO

This mantra is an invocation, awakening, and dedication. We set our intention and orientation to be aware of the Universal Creative Force (ONG) and Truth that take us from darkness to Light (GURU DEV). We humbly dedicate our practice to being aware of the Universal Creative Force and the sustaining Truth that take us from an unconscious state to consciousness.

After chanting the mantra three or more times, take a few minutes and sit quietly with your breath as it breathes through your body.

The Seed Mantra — SAT NAM

There is a primal force that has been given many names over the course of history. The goal of all religions and spiritual paths is to enjoy our oneness with this Source of all. Whatever name is given to the universal consciousness or Spirit, its essence is the eternal Truth that we all seek. So to simplify matters and to rise above the trappings of dogma, this basic Truth has been given the name SAT, which resonates with the vibration of the Oneness.

SAT NAM is the most basic mantra used in Kundalini Yoga. SAT means *the Truth*. NAM means *name, identity, to identify with*, or *to call upon*. SAT NAM (vowel sounds pronounced like "but mom") can be translated as "Truth is the name of God and Truth is my (your, our) identity."

SAT NAM is called a seed, or *bij*, mantra. Reciting these primal sounds sows the seed of universal consciousness into our mind and body and integrates the Truth into our being. SAT NAM is our anchor, reminder, command, and true essence.

We all know the axiom, "The truth shall set you free." SAT NAM sets us free through its power to clear the subconscious mind so that old wounds and programs no longer get in the way of self-realization. Its recitation awakens us up to our divine identity, where we can truly live in a state of freedom and oneness.

As a personal mantra, SAT NAM is an invocation that links us up to the true identity of our soul. SAT NAM is used as a greeting to acknowledge the Truth in each other. It has a similar meaning as "Namaste" — I bow to the Divine in you.

Mantra for Transformation — SA TA NA MA

Mantras are powerful tools for clearing and restructuring the subconscious mind. SAT NAM and its derivative SA TA NA MA are the two basic mantras taught by Yogi Bhajan to reorient the mind and thus open us up to the possibility of deep spiritual transformation. As explained above, SAT NAM seeds the Truth in our consciousness by waking us up to our divine identity.

SA TA NA MA incorporates the nuclear sounds of SAT NAM. SA TA NA MA uses these primal sounds to connect us to the evolutionary nature of existence itself. It is referred to as the *panch shabd*, which means a mantra with five sound currents. The fifth sound is "A." When we chant SA TA NA MA, we imprint the evolutionary code of the Universe into our human psyche.

SA is the beginning, infinity, the totality of everything that ever was, is, or will be.

TA is life, existence, and creativity that manifest from infinity.

NA is death, change, and the transformation of consciousness.

MA is rebirth, regeneration, and resurrection, which allow us to consciously experience the joy of the Infinite.

SA TA NA MA is so primal, its impact on our psyche is like splitting an atom. The power of this mantra comes from the fact that it rearranges the subconscious mind at the most elementary level. It has the power to break habits and addictions because it accesses the level of the mind where habits are created. And it cleanses the magnetic field where behavior patterns are encoded.

The purity and radiance of our mind depend largely upon the active functioning of the pituitary and pineal glands and hypothalamus. With the help of the hypothalamus, the pituitary gland regulates the entire glandular system.[1] The secretion of the pineal gland creates a pulsating radiance that further activates the pituitary gland. The mind goes out of balance when the pineal gland is dormant. The imbalance makes it seem impossible to break mental and physical addictions. The mantra SA TA NA MA is a powerful tool for recreating balance in the mind. There are many meditations using the seed mantra. Kirtan Kriya (on page 138) is the most basic and recommended to everyone beginning a Kundalini Meditation practice.

SAT NAM Pranayama — Breath Awareness

A basic Kundalini Yoga technique and goal is to link your breath with the mantra SAT NAM. Mentally link SAT to every inhale and NAM to every exhale. In this way, the breath and the mantra work together to calm, energize, purify, and link you up to your true identity. With practice you may naturally hear SAT on your inhale and NAM on your exhale. It is very profound to realize that you are breathing your truth with every breath.

> YOU ARE THE UNIVERSE: If you are not beautiful and graceful, there is nothing beautiful or graceful. This is a truth, for you are the universe and the universe is you.
>
> "Sermon on Two Cushions"
> October 14, 1971

[1] The tiny region in our brain called the hypothalamus serves as the master clock that regulates our physiological functions and controls our circadian rhythms, which affect the functioning of our immune system, our hormone levels, and our alertness or consciousness. The optimal functioning of our hypothalamus is determined by the cerebrospinal fluid in our brain and spine, thus the emphasis on energy flow and spinal health in Kundalini Yoga.

Healthy, Happy, Harmonious Living

Kundalini Yoga offers us techniques to stay healthy
to keep our glands secreting their vitalizing fluids
to nurture a strong nervous system
to build a strong immune system
to maintain good circulation.

A healthy body gives us the energy to fully live our life.
Our physical foundation helps us deal calmly and gracefully with the mental, emotional, and spiritual facets of our life.
There is nothing more pleasant than feeling good in our body.

Kundalini Yoga offers us techniques to be functional and authentic.
As we develop our intuition
we recognize what is real
we uncover what is important to us
we sense our innate organization and direction
our inner compass leads us toward our goals.

The journey of life is always full of challenges.
Happiness is knowing we are on our path.
Happiness is confidently dealing with our challenges as they arise.
Happiness is a serene contentment that accompanies us along the way.

Kundalini Yoga makes us feel harmonious and whole.
Kundalini Yoga activates the dormant potential of the brain.
Our body is refined into the sacred vessel of our soul.
Our unique creativity is unleashed.

We tap the reserve energy that is stored near the navel point.
The pure energy at the navel connects us to our body and Mother Earth.
The Mother energy uncoils the Kundalini, which rises to awaken our pineal gland.
When the Mother and Spirit energies connect
we have the power to attain self-realization in our human form
we have the capacity to experience Universal Consciousness.

When our finite being is at one and at peace with our Infinite Source
we live in harmony with the Universe and within ourselves.

When we feel securely connected to our Mother the Earth
we feel whole, complete, and at one with all living things.

Part III: Dealing with Life Challenges

11. Rejuvenation, Repairing Drug Damage, and Awakening the Kundalini

Regular practice of Kundalini Yoga and Meditation rejuvenates all of our body systems and repairs damage to our body and brain caused by drug use and stress. Basic Kundalini Yoga exercises help us to overcome the negative effects of all types of drugs and unhealthy living habits and to revitalize our whole system. Practiced on a regular basis, Kundalini Yoga also offers a powerful tool for lessening and even correcting the brain imbalances of bipolar, ADD, and other medically diagnosed psychological disorders.

Kundalini Yoga and Drugs

When Yogi Bhajan arrived in the U.S. in 1969, many of the young people attending his classes were using various recreational drugs to have spiritual, mystical, and psychic experiences. As a result of taking psychedelics, many people were experiencing out-of-phase and disjointed views of reality. Perceptual illusions about oneself, life, and reality occur when the nerves stimulated by the drugs continue to fire, even after the drugs have seemingly worn off.

The use of recreational drugs can artificially open and overextend the upper chakras, preventing them from processing information accurately and from properly closing. In order to bring the chakras and body systems back into balance and to offer a drug-free way to get high and spiritually connected, Yogi Bhajan began to teach powerful Kundalini Yoga kriyas. Originally he intended to teach Hatha Yoga, but he quickly recognized the need for Kundalini Yoga.

As previously discussed, the practice of Kundalini Yoga kriyas facilitates the natural opening, functioning, and balancing of the chakras, and promotes the gradual and healthy awakening of consciousness.

WARNING: Do not practice Kundalini Yoga and take recreational drugs, or drink alcohol, at the same time. Drugs interfere with, suppress, or overextend the capacities of our chakras.

Marijuana

Yogi Bhajan considered marijuana to be an insidious drug and often warned against its use. Considered by many to be a relatively harmless method to get high, marijuana stimulates the brain in a way that produces a sense of relaxation and well-being.

The problem, according to Yogi Bhajan, is that marijuana inhibits the body's mechanism that pumps the creative sexual energy into the bloodstream and to the brain. The result of ingesting or smoking marijuana over time is the progressive burn out of the brain. This is due to the fact that the functioning and nourishment of the brain is no longer supported by the flow of sexual energy through the bloodstream and spine.

In addition, habitual marijuana use can lead to memory loss and the weakening of the aura by diminishing its light to a dull gray and scrambling the body's electromagnetic energy. Long-term use also shuts down (instead of awakens) the frontal lobes of the brain, where the higher consciousness centers are located. Yogi Bhajan (and others) witnessed this widespread phenomenon in India, where many seemingly meditative sadhus, oblivious to the world, have in fact become mental vegetables through the use of hashish.

Yogi Bhajan also explained that the use of marijuana distorts the directional mechanism in our psyche. I remember very vividly when he told us at a Summer Solstice lecture in New Mexico in the early 2000s that the use of marijuana takes us off course so that when we leave our body, "we will miss our mark." The space under the big top, where over 1,000 people had gathered to be with the Master, got so quiet, you could hear a pin drop.

Damaging Effects

The purification, charging, and balancing of our body systems depend upon the free flow of the sexual ojas, or charged energy, and the effectiveness of the pumping mechanism of those energetic fluids to send them into the bloodstream and to the brain.

For any yoga to be effective, the body must be able to distribute and use the sexual energy and to activate and raise the Kundalini. The use of drugs that inhibit the flow and movement of the sexual energy fluids and the activation of the Kundalini is self-destructive. In fact, scientific studies have shown that marijuana use lowers the male sperm count.

The overuse of prescription painkillers, anti-depressants, and other drugs containing opiates are another major source of addictions. These "medicines" are in fact just as addictive as heroin is because they are made from essentially the same chemical as heroin, having the same destructive impact on the brain and negatively affecting the body's physiology.

To summarize, taking any drug that creates imbalances in the body, brain, and energy centers is counterproductive to the evolutionary awakening of consciousness and to the attainment of our spiritual goals. The practice of Kundalini Yoga reverses the harmful effects of drugs and repairs the damage done to the nervous and chakra systems. And it rejuvenates us! A cleansing diet is also effective and essential in reducing addictions and bringing about an overall physiological and psychological recovery from addictive drugs.

Kriyas and Meditations in This Manual for Repairing Drug Damage Include
Kriyas: Kriya for Drug Damage, Sat Kriya
Meditation: Medical Meditation for Habituation, To Break Drug and Other Addictive Habits
Pranayama: Four-Part Breath

12. Breaking Addictive Habits: Feel-Good Choices

Feel-Good Choices

The primal human desire to feel good is a driving force that fuels our addictions. To deal with addictions, we need to cultivate habits and behaviors that give us an experience of well-being. The commitment and dedication required to consciously create "feel-good habits" is well worth the time and effort.

Years ago I attended a class on diet and eating habits with about 40 women. The teacher asked us, "Who considers how they will feel three hours later *before* they put food in their mouth?" Only three of us raised our hands! I was shocked. These were all spiritually committed women. So don't feel bad if you wouldn't have raised your hand.

We must strive to eliminate whatever falls in the "immediate gratification with feel-bad consequences later" category. In other words, we must train ourselves to choose food, drink, and activities that benefit our state of well-being in the short, medium, and long terms. Making feel-good decisions can change our life and be a key to dealing with many addictions, including eating disorders and weight and self-esteem issues.

Monitor Your Choices Exercise

A very useful "get to know yourself" exercise is monitoring what you do to feel good. Use a journal dedicated to this purpose.

1. Start out by paying attention to and then drafting a list of choices that you make in the categories of ***food and drink***, ***exercise*** (including walking, yoga, and meditation), ***social relationships*** (including talking, texting, and other activities you do with others), and ***leisure activities*** (including any hobbies, watching TV, going to movies, gardening, eating out).
2. Identify which choices create stress and really don't feel good after the initial hit.
3. Start eliminating what doesn't create good feelings. Substitute choices that create long-term pleasurable and peaceful results.

A Healthy Diet Is Critical

When something feels missing in our life (basically a lack of connection to our soul and the Divine), we try to fill that hole with addictions of our choice. But food, alcohol, and drugs are inadequate substitutes for spiritually connected satisfaction. The problem with bad food is that none of our needs are satisfied, including the one for nourishment. In fact, unhealthy food just makes us crave more unhealthy food.

Food

Ingesting unhealthy "food" that does not have its natural, complete vitamin-mineral content not only fails to satisfy our body, it also creates cravings. This is because the body needs the complete vitamin-mineral structure to properly digest its food. If an essential nutrient is missing in the food we eat, our body will seek out the missing element by depleting the rest of the body of those particular vitamins or minerals and by sending out "hunger" signals demanding what it needs.

The problem today is that most of our foods are severely deficient in vitamin-mineral content. Genetically engineered foods (GMOs) are even worse because the natural crystalline structures of the modified plants are destroyed. As a result, our cells cannot get the nutrients they need from our food.

Fortunately, organic food and some effective vitamin and mineral supplements can help us give our body what it needs. More importantly, we can immediately start choosing healthier foods while eliminating from our diet processed sugar and other processed foods, fried foods, red meat, and too much caffeine (in quantities over the health benefits of drinking organic black and green teas in moderation).

Water and Fluids

We are born with 90% water content in our body. By the time we are 40 or 50, our cells are dehydrated down to 75% or even 60%. This is partly because we substitute sodas (which contain toxic ingredients) and other liquids (even healthy ones) for water.

However, our cells also cannot fully absorb much of the water we drink. Pollution, chemical additives (chlorine and fluoride, for example) and the processing of water has changed the structure of our water to the extent that the water molecules are too big to be fully assimilated by our cells. And no matter how much water we drink, if our cells cannot absorb it, our body's need and thirst for water is not totally quenched. Fortunately, certain water purifiers can help revitalize the water we drink.

Eliminate Refined Sugar and Processed Foods

A healthy diet requires eliminating addictive foods. All processed foods (junk food) which contain refined sugar and wheat flour are at the top of the list. Read the ingredients on the bags of chips, or on processed, packaged, and canned foods and you will notice that most of them contain wheat and various forms of processed sugars or artificial sugar substitutes, which can be considered poisons.

Refined sugar is addictive because of what I explained above. The natural nutrients have been extracted in the processing. Our body craves more in an attempt to get the minerals and vitamins it needs to carry out its digestive and eliminative functions. The caffeine from coffee, coke, and chocolate also dehydrates the body, and the chemical additives in some caffeinated products create more craving. Any amount of refined sugar can provoke craving and create addiction. This is why it is important to eliminate it completely.

Substitutes, Not Deprivation

To eliminate processed sugar and junk food from your diet, start with having a good supply of substitutes on hand. Depravation does not work. The trick is substitution. There are many "health foods" that are sweetened with honey, agave, and natural sugar from fruit. Although processed snacks made with these ingredients are not as nutritious as a piece of fruit or carrot juice, they are not harmful like refined sugar and flour. It is best to sweeten your drinks with honey, agave, or maple syrup. Definitely avoid all artificial additives and chemical sweeteners. Read the list of ingredients of every purchase. *If there are names you haven't heard of, assume they are toxic chemicals.*

Elemental Foods

In the Five Element System that classifies food according to the elements — air, water, earth, metal, and fire — fruits, all sugars, and sweet foods are all classified as "earth foods."

Our body needs earth foods and a certain amount of natural sugar. The only grain that falls in the earth category is millet. By including millet in your daily diet for a few weeks, you will notice that your sugar cravings subside.

Over time, natural sugars, like those found in millet and fruit, will be the only ones that satisfy. Without refined sugar, we feel so much better, our body is healthier, and our energy becomes more radiant. In addition, our mood swings are dramatically reduced, our brain works better, it is easier to lose weight, and we are more productive and happier.

Vegetarians

Vegetarians have a tendency to eat too many carbohydrates and to not get enough protein. When we are protein deficient, we crave sweets and carbohydrates. Excessive carbohydrates are a major cause of diabetes, Candida, obesity, and cancer.

Healthy and Unhealthy Oils

The cholesterol scare has spread the message that oil is bad. Indeed, refined, saturated, and hydrogenated oils, or fats and fried foods that are not easily digested by the body, are unhealthy — yes, *bad*. However, natural oils are needed by the body for optimal functioning. The human brain needs omega 3 and good oils, like coconut oil, to function. Eliminating good oils from our diet speeds up the aging process and, for women, makes menopause more difficult.

Olive or almond oil (not canola) in salad dressing or coconut oil added to grains or other dishes after they are cooked can satisfy these needs. Cooking with butter or olive oil is not recommended, as heat denatures olive oil and butter contains unhealthy milk solids. Cooking with ghee or coconut oil is safe because they are not denatured at high temperatures.

Ghee is clarified butter. The easiest way to make ghee is to heat several pounds of butter in a crock-pot (slow electric cooker) until the milk solids separate and collect at the bottom of the pot. These are discarded after collecting the clear, separated golden liquid, which can be stored without refrigeration.

Systemic Addictions and Choice

Addictions support each other. For example, one stop-smoking course recommends giving up coffee, caffeinated teas, alcohol, and cow dairy at the same time as each one may increase a craving for the others. This particular program also recommends eating nuts and dried and fresh fruit and increasing vitamin C intake to help replace the nutrients that have been compromised by the nicotine and must be replenished to eliminate craving.

Breaking old habits and creating new ones require making moment-by-moment choices. Yogic techniques create changes in our physiological, mental, and emotional energy that make it possible to make different choices. For instance, one woman I know reported that she actually no longer had the desire to smoke after doing Breath of Fire and Four-Part Navel Breathing daily for several weeks. So for her it was relatively easy to quit smoking, but she still had to make that choice.

Often we can still feel the pull of old habits. Will is required to make another choice. Making healthy choices is very empowering and unleashes feelings of satisfaction and self-esteem.

Start on a New Moon

The best day to begin any regime, dietary fast, or sadhana to break or make new habits is on the new moon, as this will make it is easier to keep up and succeed in a new program. Yogically, it is said that breaking a habit requires 40 continuous days of the new program. Switching gears is the first phase of changing a habit.

The Box Technique

The box technique is one way to deal with the psychology of choice — what we eat and don't eat, what we do and don't do, and what we say and don't say. We actually classify our dos and don'ts into two boxes all the time. For example, we do not eat food out of a trash bin, and we don't eat rotten food. We wouldn't even think about it. We can choose to expand our "Don't or Do Eat" box and put other foods in each box. This works if we keep items we wish to eliminate in the "Don't" box. This technique helps us circumvent a lot of mental anguish of trying to decide "to eat or not to eat." Over time, the sides of our box grow stronger, and we won't even think of the "Don't" box contents as an option.

When I was young, I often ate much more than I needed. I was of course uncomfortable after I stuffed myself. I was concerned about getting fat, which never happened. But I did waste a lot of mental and emotional energy. When I was 22 I decided that I did not want to live like that anymore. I made the decision to eat only until I was full and then I would stop. It took me about two months to get comfortable with the habit and to integrate the strategy into my psyche. I became so much more comfortable mentally, emotionally, and physically that to do any differently was no longer an option. I look at my food, appreciate what I am eating, and chew my food to enjoy and digest it fully.

Set Up to Win

We all have built-in survival strategies. The trick is to discover and develop our own strategies and to use them to our advantage. As Yogi Bhajan taught us, the universe is set up for us to win. Life on planet Earth is about discovering how to win our own game of life. We were all born with the innate wisdom to succeed and be happy.

Life Is Like a Movie

You go to a movie, give them your money, and they give you a seat and start the film for you. Between eating popcorn and drinking Coca Cola, you fall asleep. Now, you didn't pay your $5.00 to sleep in that chair did you? Why did you do it? In exactly the same way, through previous karma, life is gained here. It is paid for. You have earned it! With Guru's grace, you did the bhakti and then God granted you a human body. It is earned, paid for, and the title is clear. You can make it or you can mar it. It's your business. You've paid the money and you are now seated at the opera and the performance has begun. (If you sleep and snore through it, who cares?)

July 14, 1975

13. Releasing Stress and Restful Sleep

There are many ways that we can use our practice of Kundalini Yoga and Meditation to release accumulated stress and to let go of physical tension, which in turn helps us let go of beliefs, thoughts, and past programming that create automatic emotional responses. All of the aspects of Kundalini Yoga below help release constricted muscles and energy as well as prevent the accumulation of stress and resistance.

- **Rhythmic Movement**
  Moving, rhythmic exercises unblock stuck energy and allow it to flow again.

- **Strengthening Our Nervous System**
  A strong nervous system can naturally "shake out" or let go of muscular tension provoked by stress-producing reactions.

- **Shaking**
  Often we are instructed to vigorously shake our arms and body after an exercise or meditation. Shaking the whole body can also be done as a warm up exercise, after an exercise, or at the end of a kriya.

- **Relaxation**
  By following active exercises with relaxation, we can reprogram ourselves to release and let go of the tension of our stress-producing reactions and return to a dynamic level of peace.

- **Dancing**
  Yogi Bhajan recommended freeform dancing after a Kundalini Yoga session (which is of course structured). Dancing our own dance is a powerful way to unleash the energy of our soul.

Attitudes that Reduce Stress

A healthy body supports us in adopting mental attitudes that reduce stress, including

- Dropping judgmental and critical attitudes and beliefs
- Accepting life as it presents itself
- Giving ourselves some slack for not being "perfect" all the time — allowing ourselves to be human!
- Organizing our life around reducing stress, such as by giving ourselves 5-10 extra minutes to arrive somewhere
- Loving ourselves for doing the best we can

The more we let go, the more we free ourselves to be authentically ourselves, to live less reactive and stressful lives, and to enjoy our human experience.

Preparing for a Restful Sleep

Certain Kundalini Yoga exercises, pranayama, and meditations are designed to help release stress at the end of the day and to promote deep and restful sleep. The tips below for clearing the mind before going to bed combined with the exercises that follow will help you prepare for an entire night of peaceful sleep.

Slow Down

An hour or so before bedtime, start to slow down. Take a slow meditative walk. Stop intense mental, computer, and cell phone activity.

Eat Lightly for Evening Meal

Eat your last meal at least 1½ to 2 hours before going to bed. When you eat just before going to bed, your energy is engaged in digestion, and it is hard to sleep deeply.

Eat lightly for your evening meal; definitely no animal protein, fried, or heavy foods. Soups, salads, steamed vegetables, or other easily digested dishes are best for the evening meal.

For many people, eating dairy at night makes it more difficult to get up the next day. I discovered this when I ate a small yogurt snack before going to bed. I found it very difficult to wake up the next morning. When I eliminated yogurt, it was much easier to wake up and get up!

Put Your Mind to Rest for the Night

Feel complete about your day.

1. Acknowledge yourself for what you accomplished and lessons learned.
2. Forgive yourself for anything that didn't work out the way you intended. You did the best you could do. Hey, no one's perfect.
3. List five things you are grateful for. Gratitude and forgiveness are very soothing for the soul.

Organize and clear your mind of tomorrow's agenda.

1. Write down what you wish to accomplish the next day.
2. After you set your clear intentions, invite the Universal Organizing Power and your soul to help align energies to support you in achieving your goals.
3. Thank your angels, or whoever might be available, for special assistance.
4. Turn your concerns over to a higher power.

Exercises to Calm Yourself and Prepare for Sleep

Right and Left Nostril Breathing

As discussed in the chapter on pranayama, our two nostrils are associated with two very different energies.

When we breathe through the *right nostril*, we are *energized and stimulated*.
When we breathe through the *left nostril*, we *relax and calm down*.

Our breath naturally changes dominant nostrils approximately every 2½ hours. We can tell which nostril is our dominant one at any time simply by blocking off one, then the other. The dominant one is easy to breathe through. The non-dominant one is blocked.

Bedtime Meditation: Left Nostril Breathing

Meditating before going to bed is very beneficial, and left nostril breathing is a simple and effective meditation to do as you wind down and relax. Sit quietly, block off your right nostril, and breathe long and deeply through your left nostril. Mentally inhale SAT and exhale NAM. The mental focus on the mantra and the breath are very soothing.

Slow down your breath to four or fewer breaths per minute to facilitate relaxation, meditation, and sleep and to calm your nervous system. Lying on your right side also helps open the left nostril.

A few gentle pushups into Cobra Pose and back down will do wonders to release stress in the back.

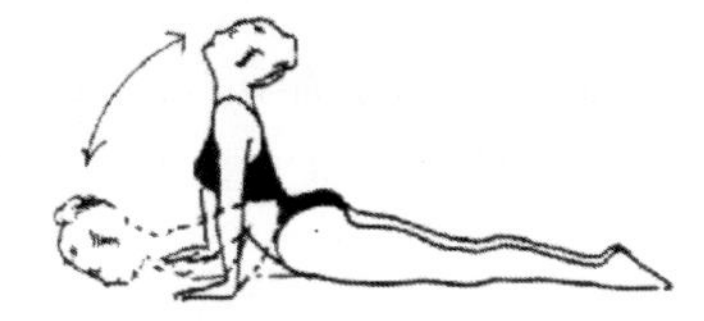

Recommended Kriyas and Meditations for Releasing Stress and Sleeping Restfully Include

Pranayama: Left Nostril Breathing
Kriyas: To Remove Negativity; Serabandanda Kriya
Meditations: Instant Heart Chakra Opener, Shabd Kriya, Kundalini Sleeping Aid (Chatachya Kriya)
Avoid inverted postures like Shoulder Stand or navel exercises that energize.
(See the guide in Appendix II for more.)

Notice how your mood and physical well-being change when your hips are happy and your navel center is activated.

14. Happy Hips: Woman's Physical, Mental, and Emotional Health

Women and Menstrual Cycle

As touched on earlier, during their moon cycle, women are advised to not do strenuous abdominal exercises and to avoid Breath of Fire, Stretch Pose, and Sat Kriya. Women need to focus on grounding and not on raising their energy during their moon cycle, which is more of an inner meditative than an active outgoing time. However, it is important to move the energy in the lower chakras. Menstrual cramps are caused by stuck energy in the reproductive system. So don't just curl up and be miserable. Spinal rotations, walking, and gentle leg exercises can help keep your energy moving and prevent discomfort.

Here is a personal story to illustrate the importance of moving during the menstrual cycle. I was teaching at Dartmouth College in New Hampshire and my sister was visiting me. It was winter, and it was snowing an absolutely beautiful snow that sent out the message, "Go cross-country skiing!" Whenever it snowed like this, I dropped what I was doing and went skiing. This day was also the first day of my cycle, and I was having serious cramps. But with my sister's help, I got out the door, and we trekked the 10-minute walk to the ski paths. After just a few minutes of skiing, my cramps totally disappeared. I felt invigorated, and the cramps never came back for the remainder of the cycle. The message of the story is MOVE!

Puberty and Teenage Years

The transition from little girl to womanhood is challenging in many ways. Hormonal changes that initiate the menstrual cycle cause dramatic shifts in a girl's physical and emotional states. Her emotions can go haywire for no apparent reason, leaving the preteen and teenage girl thinking that she might be going nuts and wondering why. Menstrual cramping can be painful and even debilitating. So what is a girl supposed to do? The exercises in the Happy Hips kriya (page 131) are for you!

Menopause

At menopause, a woman's estrogen levels diminish to the point that her menstrual cycle stops. Estrogen feeds the kidneys. When a woman feels hot and has hot flashes, it is because her kidneys do not have enough estrogen. There are many opinions concerning estrogen supplementation. Yogically, we avoid the chemical estrogens and supplement with natural estrogens for the time it takes to make the transition to post-menopause. The Chinese have perfected herbal estrogen remedies that have saved many women from hot flash drama.

A woman's transition through menopause often makes her more meditative. Her energy decreases temporarily and she becomes less active. The timing varies from one to several years, after which she "comes back to life" and enters a new phase of enjoying her mature womanhood.

Physical Stress and Imbalance

As I explained in my book *The Gift of Womanhood,*[2] to be physically, mentally, and emotionally balanced, *woman must be able to relax into her own rhythm and energy flow.* A woman is designed with the creative potential to make things happen. But her energy can be depleted by stressful living — adapting to rigid schedules, juggling excessive activities, and walking on the razor's edge of too many responsibilities, demands, and expectations. All of the above can disturb a woman's biorhythms. When her rhythm is disrupted and her energy is chaotic and she cannot relax, *she becomes uncontrollably emotional.*

Living in a state of continual stress is very damaging to a woman's constitution. Physical, mental, and emotional stress are all factors influencing menstrual problems, early and painful menopause, and breast and reproductive organ cancers. Stress also weakens a woman's nervous system, taxes her kidneys and glandular system, disturbs her hormonal balance, and compromises her intuition. When a woman's body is compromised by anxiety and tension, she cannot relax and live in the natural flow of her being.

Physical Health and Exercises for Women

A woman needs physical exercise that is appropriate for her body. All parts of her body must be stimulated on a regular basis to maintain both physical and emotional health. (See the Spinal Awakening and Centering kriya on page 128 and the Happy Hips kriya on page 131.) If a woman's body does not get the physical exercise it needs, her emotional body will unconsciously try to give her the stimulation that her physical body craves. She will become emotional for no apparent reason. Lack of appropriate daily exercise contributes to stress, emotionality, general irritability, anger, frustration, and depression. The connection between exercise and emotions also helps explain the relationships between being overweight and having an uneven temperament, being unhappy or depressed, and lacking energy.

A woman's physical and emotional problems are often caused by an imbalance in her hormonal system. A daily routine of Kundalini Yoga and Meditation helps to correct these imbalances and provides the needed stimulation to her glandular, digestive, elimination, circulatory, and nervous systems.

Because women are women and *not* men, exercise regimes that suit a man's body are often not appropriate for a woman's body. It is sometimes recommended that a woman exercise until she sweats on her forehead. Daily sweating is healthy. But each woman must monitor for herself how much energy she can exert without overtaxing her system. Women with a fiery constitution in their teens, 20s, and 30s often have an abundance of physical energy and can

---

[2] See Guru Rattana, *The Gift of Womanhood: Inner Mystery, Outer Mastery* (Sunbury, PA: YogaTech.com), 2012, for further discussion on important issues affecting a woman's physical, emotional, and spiritual well-being.

handle more rigorous routines. Excessive physical exertion can be harmful for women with more delicate constitutions and in pre-, post-, or menopausal stages of life.

Women can easily monitor the state of their kidneys and adrenal glands by paying attention to the intensity of exercise that they are able to support, which varies from day to day and changes during their moon cycle. The kidneys are like batteries — the amount of energy that they supply is not unlimited. As a woman's estrogen level decreases at menopause, she reaches into her kidney power for energy, which can be easily depleted. If an exercise regime is too taxing, a woman will feel hot, burned out, and need a lot of rest to recuperate. If these conditions are experienced, a woman should modify her exercise routine to create stimulation and avoid depletion and exhaustion.

Happy Hips and Emotional Balance

A woman's pelvic and abdominal region is the location of her womb and the source of her power. Her hips naturally move to accommodate childbirth. Compare a woman and a man walking and you will see a noticeable difference in hip movement. For physical health and emotional balance, a woman's daily routine must incorporate exercises to move her hips and the energy in her belly.

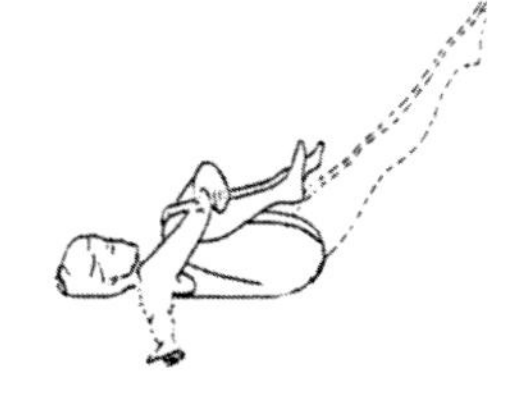

Women need to do Happy Hips exercises every day to maintain their physical health and emotional balance. In addition to a regular routine, it is a good idea to stretch the legs and hips after sitting poses and meditating. (See the Happy Hips kriya on page 131.)

When the hipbones and joints in the hip area aren't adjusted and set properly, the spine is adversely affected. This can cause backaches, and the body will be off balance as well. Leg stretches and navel exercises work on the entire hip and abdominal area to adjust the hipbones; massage the internal organs; stimulate the reproductive, digestive, and elimination systems; and keep the lower spine healthy. Leg stretches also help overcome and prevent sciatic nerve pain, keeping that nerve in a healthy condition. Moreover, exercises that move the hips strengthen the abdominal muscles, align the navel center, and help one stay grounded.

Women who sit a lot during the day should get up and walk around, dance, or shake their body periodically to move their hips, then notice how their mood changes!

Many Kundalini Yoga exercises work on the hips in some way. The Spinal Awakening and Centering set awakens the spine and prepares the body for the Happy Hips exercises.

Emotional Energy and Self-Nurturing

To create a safe home for their emotions, women must relax their belly so their emotional energy can also relax and flow. To do so women must overcome the habit of holding in their belly, which creates stress and blocks her natural flowing nature. When a woman can let go of the insidious programming that compels her to try to flatten her belly, she can naturally create a feeling of a secure and cozy womb within and experience the satisfaction of self-nurturing. Women who can relax into their own flow feel the essence of their womanhood.

Sufi Grinds is a great exercise to unleash and enjoy flowing, nurturing energy. By simply relaxing into the circular flow of their energy, women may find that their sexual energy will naturally spiral up their spine and through their body. Women can also lightly pull the muscles in the vagina (kegels) to release and direct their sexual energy up their spine, being careful not to block the flow by being too forceful.

BHAGAUTI: The form of woman is Bhagauti, the Goddess with eight hands walking on the back of a tiger (which represents ego). She has four hands bearing arms, swords, and spears. The sword is defense, the spear distance. In her other four hands she holds grace — flowers, beads, and lotus blossoms for purity. So half of her represents gifts, and half, defense. She is the symbol of compassion and power, self-defense and grace, knowledge and arms, this Goddess who rides on a tiger.

October 1971

15. For Men: Harness Your Horniness

Self-Nurturing for Both Sexes

At our second chakra, we experience both (1) emotional energy, which must relax and flow, and (2) sexual energy, which must be directed upward.

Our first and ongoing task at the second chakra/belly/abdominal area is to release stuck emotional energy, which causes stress and frustration. Both men and women therefore need to cultivate their ability to use their emotional energies for self-nurturing. Both sexes must allow their emotional energies to freely move unencumbered so they can relax into their own flow and rhythm.

Men may be conditioned to believe that they can skip this step. But if man fails to release the flow of his emotional energy, raising his sexual energy and Kundalini may not happen. And the awakening in the upper chakras cannot be sustained.

Therefore, man must also learn to consciously relax his abdominal area, let go of stress, and allow his emotional energy to flow. As he trains himself to let go of the cultural programming to flatten his belly, man can create a cozy space within, where he feels secure enough to awaken to his own feelings and experience of self-nurturing. Again, Sufi Grinds is a great exercise for men to stimulate and enjoy flowing, nurturing energy.

Sexual Pleasure and Higher Consciousness

A man's vital sexual energy nourishes his body and brain and provides a source of self-regeneration. Therefore, he should not waste it! Men naturally feel the loss of energy after ejaculation. Man's body needs many hours and sometimes days to replenish his supply. The extent to which men are advised to limit the release of semen through ejaculation depends upon age and physical condition. Thus, a man needs to intuitively and physically learn to respect his own body and its limits as he grows older.

An important part of the exercises and Kundalini Yoga kriyas designed for men to channel their sexual energy include the application of root lock. For men, the lock at the second chakra involves pulling the muscles at the base of the penis like when trying to stop urination. Combined with the first chakra lock (lightly tightening the anus), man focuses on directing his sexual energy, ojas, up to his third eye.

The sixth and second chakras work together to direct sexual energy up the spine and awaken higher consciousness. Focusing at the third eye provides a stable centering focus and establishes the direction for raising both sexual energy and Kundalini to awaken the mind to higher love.

A delicate root lock, which neither blocks nor overstimulates, but coaxes sexual energy up the spine can produce *spinal orgasms* that are very pleasurable. Yet, because of the nature of a man's sexual energy and the fact that it is vital for self-nurturing, a different focus is required. Men who are able to channel their sexual energy up their spine to feed their brain awaken their neutral mind and experience the essence of their manhood.

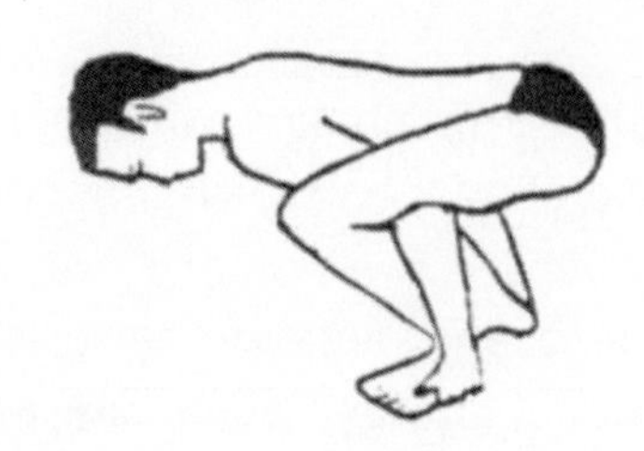

Men will also be reassured to know there is an effective exercise that immediately helps them to harness their horniness! Chair Pose, done with Breath of Fire for 2-5 minutes, relieves the pressures of excess sexual energy in the lower chakras. (See page 124.) Other Kundalini Yoga exercises and kriyas designed to channel sexual energy up the spine also play an important role in achieving high states of consciousness. In fact, many traditional spiritual paths were designed by men for men for this very purpose.

Potency and Prostate Health

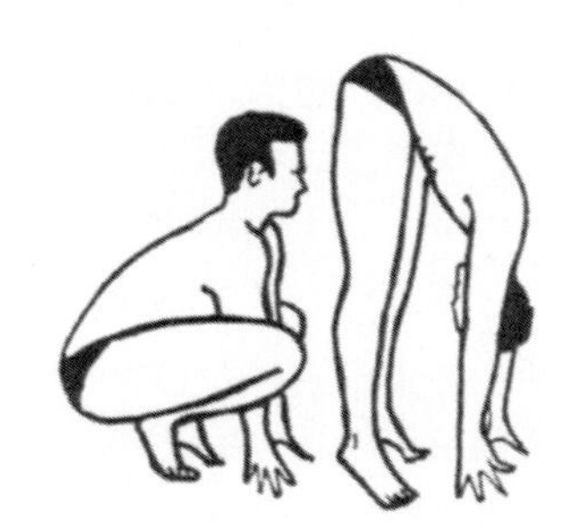

Many Kundalini Yoga exercises and kriyas are designed by men for men to cultivate and maintain sexual potency. Frog Pose is one of these exercises that was practiced by men in India before marriage to build (and demonstrate) their sexual potency. A minimum "performance" for his soon-to-be bride was 5 minutes of Frog Pose. (See page 107 for full instructions on doing Frog Pose.)

Potency exercises stimulate the blood flow in the prostate gland, which is essential to maintaining its health. Men are also advised to massage the soft area just above the public bone to increase the blood flow to the prostate gland.

Here's one male student's testimonial regarding the benefits of Frog Pose:

> As a middle-aged man, I started developing near-chronic discomfort in my lower back, likely a re-aggravation of a severe muscle strain from a few years ago. I often used the soreness as an excuse to not exercise or practice yoga. However, after adding just 26 repetitions of Frog Pose to my morning warm up set (which I could do without feeling it in my lower back), the chronic discomfort went away. Even after straining my lower back again, the soreness only lasted a day or two rather than a week or longer.
>
> After a few days of doing Frog Pose, I also began noticing sporadic, subtle vibrations in my groin area, and sometimes down my legs, throughout my day. I feel that the energy is both waking up and moving, but not in an arousing sort of way. In fact, sexual urges seem less distracting than they once were, though I feel ready when the time comes. Hopefully I'm discovering the "on-off" switch.

16. The Navel Center and Our Core

Activating, aligning, and establishing a relationship with our navel chakra is basic to Kundalini Yoga. Because Yogi Bhajan understood the vital role of the navel center in the awakening of the Kundalini, his early Kundalini Yoga kriyas were focused on awakening and empowering the navel center. When the fire at the navel is sufficiently activated, prana (life force) and apana (eliminating force) mix and descend to the base of the spine to activate the Kundalini. Strengthening the navel center is always part of our daily practice.

The Many Functions of the Navel Center

The navel center plays a determining role in many aspects of human design and functioning. The alignment of our navel center is necessary (1) for the optimal functioning of our metabolism, (2) for our general health, (3) to break and make habits, (4) to stay centered and focused, (5) to be motivated and courageous, and (6) for the development of our personal identity structure.[3]

Where Is the Navel Center?

When we say navel center, we are referring to a point 1-3 inches below the belly button. This energy center is the gravity balance point in the body. When we pump our navel energy or move from our navel center, we are actually pumping and moving from a center where thousands of nerves come together. As you practice navel exercises, the nerve endings will be stimulated and the energy will coalesce at this point.

The navel center is the easiest chakra to monitor. You know your navel center is "set" when you feel a pulse at or around the rim of the umbilicus. Although you can check the pulse sitting or standing, the easiest position is lying down, ideally before and after doing navel exercises.

Simply take the middle finger of either hand, place it on the navel or navel center, and search for a pulse. If there is no pulse, the pulse is weak, or it is not in or around the navel, your navel needs to be "set." You will experience that after navel exercises your pulse is stronger and the position may have also shifted to the navel center.

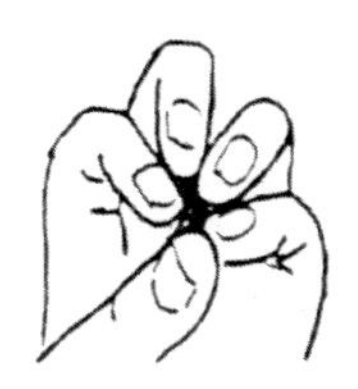

After a few leg lifts, one woman had her pulse jump from the lower right corner of her abdomen to the center of her navel! So do not be alarmed if you cannot find your pulse. You will find it with the help of Kundalini Yoga exercises.

It is normal to have a weak pulse in the morning after sleeping. That is why it is strongly recommended to set your navel center before you start your day. Also during the day, if you

---

[3] See Guru Rattana, *Your Life Is in Your Chakras* (Sunbury, PA: YogaTech.com), 2014, for a detailed discussion of the navel chakra.

feel off center, pump your navel center by doing Breath of Fire to come back to center.

Nabhi Kriya (see page 99) was taught by Yogi Bhajan in 1971 and remains one of the classic sets for balancing and activating the navel center. Practice this set for 40 days and it will change your life! Everyone needs to include a kriya or exercises for the navel center in his or her daily practice. *Sat Kriya,* one of the first "all-in-one exercise" kriyas taught by Yogi Bhajan, is another classic kriya that awakens the Kundalini from the navel point.

Abdominal Core Release

An aligned navel center consolidates the energy in our whole abdominal area (first three chakras) and plays a vital role in staying centered and releasing stress.

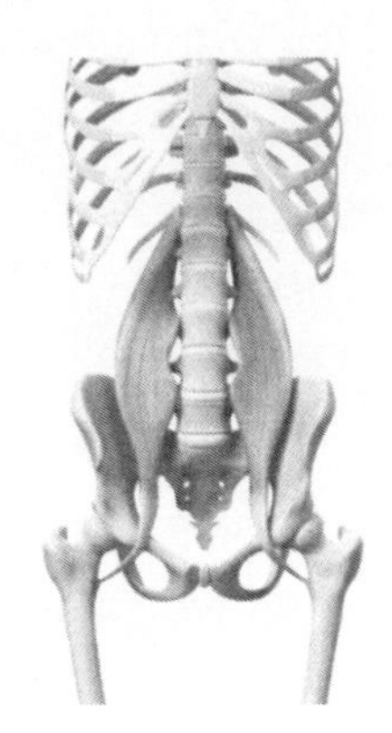

The core muscles in our belly and the psoas muscles are some of the major muscle groups involved in our stress responses. The psoas muscles attach to the front, back, and lower part of our spine. They connect the back of our spine with our pelvis and legs and guard our innermost core and center of gravity. These lower-chakra fight-or-flight muscles contract to protect us from danger. When the "danger" is over, this deep set of muscles and our adrenals must let go of the tension so that it does not accumulate. The release of the psoas muscles reverberates throughout our whole body, bringing it back into a relaxed state.

Kundalini Yoga exercises that engage and thus prepare the core abdominal and psoas muscles for toning, strengthening, and release include Stretch Pose, leg lifts, and many others. (See Nabhi Kriya.)

Navel Breathing

Pumping the Navel

Kundalini Yoga often uses breathing patterns that activate the navel center. Four-Part Breath, as described in the 4/4 Breath for Energy meditation (page 141), is a good example of how a segmented breath can be used to activate the navel chakra. "Pumping" in this case means to lightly pull the navel toward the spine and let it release before the next pump.

We also pump the navel when we chant mantras, such as variations of "Har." Again, we very lightly pull in the navel point to create an activation of the fire. (See "Har" meditation on page 82 and Brainwave Meditation on page 140.)

Pumping the navel creates a pulse, which we can simultaneously feel at our third eye. We thus use the pulsing at the navel to activate and help awaken the sixth chakra.

Navel as an Activator

Pumping the navel is used to engage root lock. As the illustration of the psoas muscles above reveals, these muscles connect the spine from the navel to the base. So whether we first engage the navel or the root, the result is the same: the root lock is activated.

The navel thus serves as an activator mechanism to (1) engage the root lock, (2) create the fire that descends to awaken the Kundalini and then rises to open the heart, and (3) to generate the fire and pulse that awakens the third eye.

Navel as a Centering Mechanism

In long deep breathing, we consciously expand at the navel on the inhale and pull the navel toward the spine on the exhale. Navel focus activates the centering mechanism in our physical body. When the 72,000 nerve endings come together at the navel center, our psyche shifts from scattered to focused. We are better able to concentrate and act as a coherent whole.

Breath of Fire

Breath of Fire is another breathing technique designed to activate the navel center. Even one minute of Breath of Fire can bring you back to your center.

Breath of Fire

Inhale and Exhale

The exhale is active and the inhale is passive. The navel is pulled in on the quick exhalation. The navel relaxes on the inhalation.

Length of Inhale and Exhale

In Breath of Fire, the inhale is the same length or importance as the exhale. By simply relaxing the navel, the inhale happens and the same quantity of air is allowed to return.

Light and Rhythmic

Breath of Fire is rapid and rhythmic. Although the pace can vary from the normal 2-3 times per second, the lightness is maintained. The body and face are relaxed while the navel does the work. The breath flows easily and can be maintained for long periods of time, up to 31 minutes, while maintaining a relaxed state. Once you get into the rhythm, you enjoy it and want to keep going.

Solar Plexus and Lower Diaphragm

Breath of Fire uses the navel and solar plexus as a pump and is a function of the lower diaphragm. Although we can feel movement in the abdominal muscles, we do *not* actively engage them. If we engage the abdominal muscles and the breath is too low, the breath slows down and we have trouble continuing.

Cleansing and Energizing

Breath of Fire is simultaneously cleansing and energizing.

Har Mantra and Pumping the Navel

The following mantra is perfect for pumping the navel, creating the tappa heat to awaken the Kundalini, and awakening the whole spine.

Sit in Easy Pose (or any seated posture), bring your hands into Gyan Mudra, (thumbs and forefingers touching), and chant in a monotone, enunciating each sound rhythmically:

HARI HARI HARI HAR

HARI and HAR represent the embodiment of the Infinite. "Har" mantras relate to the Earth and are for manifesting and prosperity.

As you softly repeat HARI HAR, place your tongue on the roof of your mouth to make the "R" sound. It won't sound like an American or Spanish "R," but it will stimulate the upper palate in a way that activates the pituitary and pineal glands.

On each syllable of the mantra, lightly pull the navel toward the spine and release. Focus on your navel as your *center*. Build navel power by creating heat. It is critical to generate and feel the heat because it is this tappa that descends to the base of the spine to activate the Kundalini.

As you lightly pump the navel and feel the muscles involved, you will feel these muscles connect down to the base of the spine. As you become aware of these muscles, you will experience that you can simultaneously pull the root lock at the anus. The heat at the navel activates the sensation of the connection. Pumping the navel and anus together engages the full root lock. As the spine becomes more alive, energy will flow up to the heart. Feel the "H" sound at the heart.

As you pump, also feel the pulse simultaneously at both the navel and at the third eye. Basically, play with the sounds and the delicate pumping to create awakening in your spine and to move the energy up the spine to the third eye.

Continue for 5, 11, 15, 22, or 31 minutes. Then sit or lie down and enjoy your experience.

These same instructions can be used while doing Sat Kriya and any other navel pumping exercise.

It is absolutely essential to relax the belly while pumping the navel and applying root lock. A tense belly blocks the energy flow. And there is no awakening of the Kundalini when the locks are constrictions rather than activations!

17. Awareness Training and Discovery

Spiritual awakening requires training oneself to become more and more aware. Every aspect of our life is a function of our level of awareness. Expanded awareness makes it possible to upgrade (1) what we experience, (2) what and how we create, and (3) how we live our life.

Enhancing our experience of our self and our life, expressing our unique creativity, and acting effectively to meet life challenges all require our ability to continually increase our awareness of what is going on in our inner reality and how we react/respond to life situations. We commit to and engage in awareness training in order to

1. Deepen and expand our experience of our inner and outer realities
2. Move into higher states of consciousness
3. Actively and more successfully participate in co-creating our life

Awareness is both an action (a verb) and a faculty (a noun). *As a verb or action*, awareness refers to our active participation in paying attention and focusing. *As a noun or a faculty*, awareness refers to our ability to perceive and have sensory experiences.

Guidelines to Cultivate and Expand Awareness

During your Kundalini Yoga and Meditation practice, you are invited to pay more attention in order to upgrade your level of awareness. Your expanded capacity to be aware will make it possible to discover and enjoy more profound experiences.

1. Pay Attention to Your Breath

Start by paying attention to your breath however it grabs your attention in your body. The important thing is to activate and strengthen your faculty of attention.

2. Pay Attention to Neutral Space

An initial and required step in awareness training is to awaken our neutral mind and identify the neutral space in our mind. In our neutral channel, we can pay attention with fewer filters, judgments, and inaccurate interpretations. We build our neutral space to circumvent our dualistic mind, its collaboration with our subconscious emotional conditioning, and the problems that they create.

To access your neutral inner space, close your eyes and pay attention to open expansive space, the sound of silence, stillness, darkness, or whatever quality gets your attention and is there when you come back the next time. Don't make something up, because it will not be there another time.[4] Continue to pay attention to whatever quality you witness in your neutral mind as you allow your thoughts to pass through with non-attachment.

3. Pay Attention to the Sensations in Your Body

We train our neutral observer mind to pay attention to

- The sensations in our body, our skin
- Our breath as it moves in our body
- Feelings that emanate from emotions — alive energy that moves

4. Pay Attention with Both Neutral and Feeling Awareness

You will soon realize that you can simultaneously pay attention to your neutral space, and from this non-judgmental position, you can be present to the aliveness in your body.

Awareness Directives

As you practice Kundalini Yoga, remember that awareness involves both training and discovery.

> **Training** is about cultivating your ability to pay attention.
> **Discovery** is about using your expanded awareness to have deeper perceptual, sensory, and feeling experiences.

Use the following awareness directives and exercises to guide your inner journey and deepen your spiritual practice:

Begin each session by taking a few minutes to sit quietly with your breath as it breathes through your body. This is passive or allowing breathing. You are not controlling or altering your breath. Be with your breath in your body exactly the way it is. Turn your attention to your body, to the sensations in your body, to the space inside your skin. Focus totally on yourself.

During the warm ups and kriya, focus on the interactive effects of the active and passive parts of the exercises. Practice going deeper into the passive space — letting go, allowing, relaxing, being with what *is* happening in your body and energy field. Learning how to allow and let go of resistance creates a profound shift in consciousness!

Below is a list of directives that you can tell yourself to train your mind to move into deeper experiences. During each session, pick one or more commands depending upon what you wish

---

[4] See Guru Rattana, *The Power of Neutral* (Sunbury, PA: YogaTech.com), 2013, for further discussion on how to develop and stay connected in the neutral channel.

to work on at that time. Do not pick too many for one session. Choose directives that create a positive response in your mind and body. As you develop your practice, you can add your own directives to the list.

Awareness Directives

- Be aware
- Observe
- Pay attention
- Listen
- Feel

Feeling and Grounding Directives

- Stay present in your body
- Feel what you are feeling inside your skin
- Feel the sensations in your body
- Be with your breath in your body
- Enjoy what you are feeling
- Feel where you are sitting and be here at this moment with this breath
- Contain all your sensations inside your skin

Grounding requires feeling the sensations in your body and is accomplished by staying present to everything that you feel in your legs, feet, abdomen, solar plexus, heart, throat, and neck.

Be aware of the subtle energies in your body. Anchor the pleasurable feelings simply by feeling these sensations in your body. Specifically pay attention to your legs, feet, skin, the base and full length of the spine, belly, and pulse at your navel.

"Let Go" Directives

- Let go
- Allow
- Relax
- Accept
- Do nothing
- Release resistance
- Let the energy flow
- Be with what *is* as it is

- Wait, be patient, and be present in the experience

Between exercises, relax into the space of letting go. Allow your breath to normalize. Allow the integration to happen. Allow your total being to come into balance and harmony. *Trust* the intelligence of your body. It knows exactly what to do.

Containing and Consolidating Directives

- Let all the alive energies integrate and strengthen your space and aura
- Feel your light expand and deepen with each subsequent exercise
- Feel the electrical charge as radiance that forms a boundary of light around your aura
- Feel a stable, grounded, in-the-body sensation in your body
- Allow and feel every sensation inside your skin to contain and consolidate your energy

Awareness and "Let Go" Exercise

With daily practice, you can quickly increase your level of awareness. An easy way to train yourself to be more aware is to do any Kundalini Yoga exercise or meditation for one minute or more, and then sit and focus your attention on one directive. Go deep into the experience. When you drift off or start thinking, do another exercise (or the same one) for another minute (or whatever time you wish). Then again sit and direct your attention and feeling to the experience that you have selected to cultivate.

To summarize, practice 1 (or more) minute of exercise, pay attention for 1-2 minutes, do another 1 (or more) minute of exercise, followed again by 1-2 minutes of focusing on your experience, and so on.

Do this for 5-30 minutes every day and you will make significant progress. After a few days, you won't believe how easy it is to stay present and be in your expanded sensory awareness.

Continually Align Your Spine

Aligning your spine and posture is critical for spinal health and facilitating the flow of Kundalini energy. As you practice Kundalini Yoga and Meditation, continually be aware of the position of and sensations in your spine. Use the locks/bhandas to create subtle adjustments of the muscles and position of your body and spine, with the intent of directing the easy flow of energy up and down the spine.

To achieve optimal results, think of the locks as alignments that facilitate the following effects:

- Navel — to position body on sit bones, maintain root during exercises, center
- Root (rectum, perineum, sex organ) — to ground, create a base, move energy upwards
- Diaphragm (on exhale) — to open heart and move fire from the navel to the heart
- Neck — to align spine, open heart, bow head to heart
- Eyes — to focus attention and center, usually at the third eye
- Tongue — lightly press the tongue to the roof of the mouth to channel energy up to the crown chakra

As you apply the locks with various intensities and with the suspended breath, play with the energies in your body and spine. Be aware of and enjoy (1) the awakening, (2) the increased clarity and purity of mind, (3) the activation in your body, (4) the energetic flow and movement of energies, and (5) the light and radiance of your being.

An artist is an artist. The art represents the artist. Is that true or not? Deny it if you can. You are the art and God is the artist. You are the finite and God is the Infinity. God is the source and your route is to represent the source. Religion is a science of reality and the art of happiness.

18. Summary Tips to Begin

***Choosing a Kriya and Meditation* —** Choose what you wish to work on, what you can do, and what fits into your schedule. Every kriya and meditation produces results. Enjoy your experience.

Perform the Exercises in the Sequence Given — You can shorten each exercise as needed to suit your physical condition. If you cannot do an exercise, either visualize yourself doing it and feel the muscles that you would use to do it, or do an alternate exercise that stimulates a similar response.

Adapt to Your Physical Capacity — For those who have a very limited physical capacity, choose any exercise that you can do. Use powerful breathing, perform the locks, and pay close attention to your spine and sensations in your body after the exercise.

Listen to Your Body — Do only what you can safely do. Your body knows. Listen to it. Avoid strain and injury. Even a few seconds creates an activation. Slowly work up to longer times, or stay with times that are comfortable.

***Mental Focus* —** To focus your mind during each exercise, mentally vibrate SAT on the inhale and NAM on the exhale. While doing Breath of Fire or a faster breathing technique, you may wish to mentally chant SA TA NA MA.

***Locks at the End of Each Exercise* —** The locks are performed at the end of each exercise. This is usually not written in the instructions. The unstated instruction is to perform the mahabhand on both the suspended inhale and exhale. Sometimes this varies, in which case the specific instructions are given. Also, one can choose to apply the locks only once or several times.

Integration Time — Following the activation of each exercise, allow time for the energy to integrate and for the body to make adjustments. Come out of the posture into a comfortable pose and simply be passively present to your energy, your breath, and the sensations in your body. This helps contain and ground your energy.

Enjoy Your Experience — Each exercise activates energy, which creates the possibility of increased awareness and aliveness. Enjoy what you experience in the moment. *Be here now.*

Let Go — Train yourself to relax, let go, and do nothing (except pay attention to your breath and the sensations in your body) between exercises and during the deep relaxation at the end of a kriya.

Keep Up! — The important thing is to practice every day! Love yourself and your life!

Kriyas and Meditations

A Renewed Life

Kundalini Yoga helps us stop the inner war

that causes stress and struggle and wastes energy and life force.
We empower ourselves from within to experience

neutrality
calmness
stillness
clarity and
peace.

Kundalini Yoga allows us to establish a state of mind where

we are conscious of our soul
we can act from higher consciousness
we cease to be puppets of external and emotional stimuli
we intuitively know the effects of an action before we take it
we mindfully choose our thoughts and actions
we make our choices from knowing who we are and why we are here.

Kundalini Yoga offers us the techniques to establish the physical, mental, and emotional strength and integration that make it possible

to release our fears and insecurities
to experience our inner divinity
to meet our challenges creatively
to live our life resourcefully and passionately
to experience each stage of life with grace and gratitude.

Kundalini Yoga is a path of discipline that helps us

alter and cultivate consciousness
achieve mental as well as physical flexibility
heighten our spiritual awareness and presence
find higher meaning and purpose in life.

Kundalini Yoga is about establishing a conscious relationship between our finite self and our infinite soul.

It is the science of strengthening our radiance that gives us

a greater capacity
a positive projection
an expanded impact
a rich and fulfilled life.

Part IV: Kriyas and Meditations

Tune In: Adi Mantra

We begin each practice of Kundalini Yoga by chanting the Adi Mantra three or more times. The purpose of chanting this mantra is to "change channels," awaken our neutral mind, and establish our connection to the Golden *Chain*. We do it as many times as needed to feel connected.

Directions
Inhale deeply and chant on one breath

ONG NA MO GURU DEV NA MO

A short sip of air through the mouth is permitted if necessary after the ONG NA MO. But the breath must not be drawn out, as it will interrupt the rhythm of the mantra.

ONG is the creative aspect of the Universe.
NA MO means "we call upon it" and "to identify with."
GURU DEV is the subtle divine wisdom of the Universe.
NA MO again states our intention to align and to become one with divine wisdom.

The ONG is to be vibrated powerfully in the nasal passages, sinuses, and upper palate. Although the mouth is open, the air comes out through the nose. The vibration of ONG causes the pituitary and pineal glands to secrete, thus awakening the neutral mind. Note that DEV is chanted in one tone only, i.e., it does not drop down a note at the end:

COMMENTS: The transmission of information and consciousness from master teachers, who have preceded us, to students is referred to as the Golden Chain. Yogi Bhajan, a master of Kundalini Yoga, who was the first to openly share this technology with the world, was a living connection to the Golden Chain.

Connecting with the master is of additional importance to those who are learning and practicing Kundalini Yoga on their own. By chanting ONG NA MO GURU DEV NA MO, you are guided in your practice. The more you are able to receive and pay attention, the more you will be aware of this guidance. By the way, if you ever dream of Yogi Bhajan, it is not a mere dream. His subtle body is coming to assist you in some way.

Basic Postures and Mudras

Sitting Postures

Various sitting postures are designed to stimulate the glands, organs, and body systems and to position the spine for meditation. The various sitting poses often apply pressure on nerves or acupressure points, stimulating the brain and body for certain effects. The most common meditation sitting postures are

Easy Pose (or Sukasana): Cross the legs comfortably at the ankles or both feet on the floor, pressing the lower spine forward to keep the back straight.

Often the directions for sitting postures say simply, "Sit in Easy Pose," which means to sit in a pose that is the most comfortable for you to be able to perform the exercise.

Perfect Pose (or Siddhasana): Right heel presses against the perineum, sole against left thigh. Left heel is placed on top of the right heel and presses the body above the genitals with the toes tucked into the groove between the right calf and thigh. Knees should be on the ground with one heel directly above the other. This is the most comfortable asana for many and promotes the ascent of the Kundalini.

Lotus (or Padmasana): Lift left foot onto upper right thigh, then place right foot on left thigh as close to the body as possible. This locked-in posture automatically creates an aligned spine and thus enhances deep meditation. The right leg is usually on top, but you can switch legs.

Rock Pose (or Vajrasana): Kneel and sit on heels (tops of feet on the ground) so that they press the nerves in the center of the buttocks.

Celibate (or Hero Pose): Sit with bent knees, but not on the feet. Kneeling between the feet helps channel sexual energy up the spine.

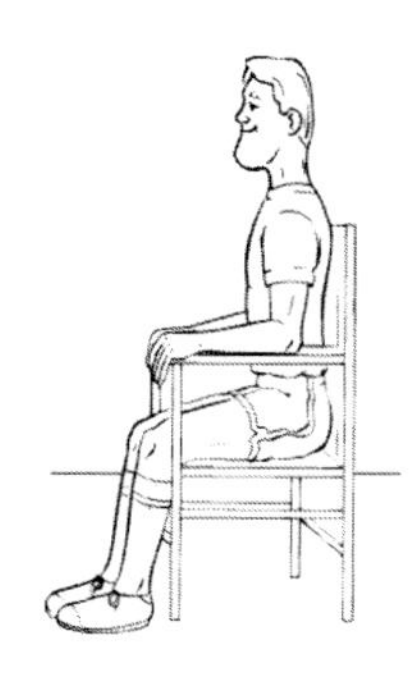

For those who have a hard time sitting in a cross-legged position on the floor, you can sit on a yoga bench or in a straight-backed chair for many of the exercises and for meditation. If you sit in a chair, be sure that both feet are flat and evenly placed on the ground, and keep the spine straight.

Hand Mudras

Mudras are hand positions that lock and guide energy flow to the brain. By curling, crossing, stretching, and touching the fingers and hands, we can communicate with the body and brain as each area of the hand corresponds to a certain part of the brain or body. Some commonly used mudras are

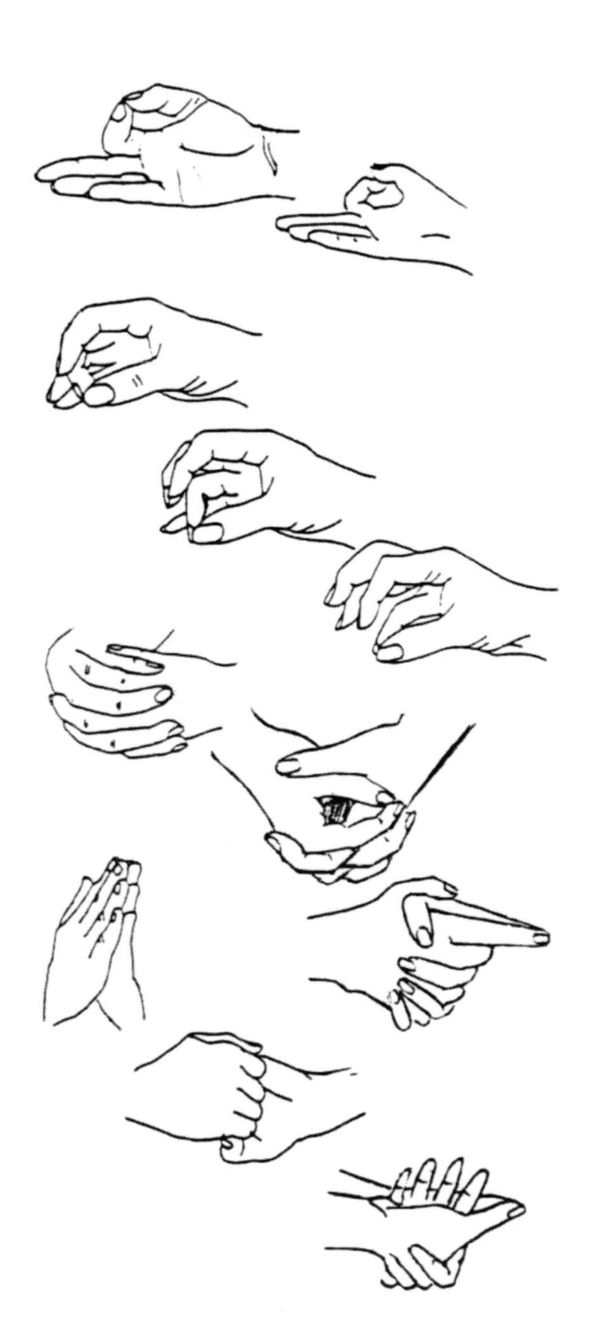

Gyan Mudra: The tip of the thumb, which represents ego and will, touches the tip of the index finger, stimulating knowledge and wisdom. The index finger is symbolized by Jupiter, and the thumb represents the ego. Gyan Mudra imparts receptivity and calm.

Active Gyan Mudra: The first joint of the index finger is bent under the first joint of the thumb, imparting active knowledge.

Shuni Mudra: Tip of middle finger (symbolized by Saturn) touches the tip of the thumb, giving patience.

Surya or Ravi Mudra: Tip of the ring finger (symbolized by Uranus or the Sun) touches the tip of the thumb, giving energy, health, and intuition.

Buddhi Mudra: Tip of little finger (Mercury) touches tip of thumb for clear and intuitive communication.

Venus Lock: *For men*, interlace fingers with left little finger on the bottom, the right index finger on top, pressing the left thumb into the webbing between the thumb and forefinger of the right hand. *For women*, interlace fingers with right little finger on the bottom, the left index finger on top, pressing the right thumb into the webbing between the thumb and forefinger of the left hand. The pressure in the

Venus mounds at the base of the thumbs help to channel energy, create glandular balance, focus, and concentration.

Prayer Mudra: Palms are pressed together at the heart center, thumbs touching the sternum. Centers and balances the right and left hemispheres of the brain to access the neutral mind.

Bear Grip: Left palm faces out from body with thumb down, and right palm faces body, thumb up, and fingers are curled and hooked together to stimulate the heart and intensify concentration.

Buddha Mudra: *For men*, right hand rests on left palm. *For women*, left hand rests on the right palm. Palms are up, thumb tips touching each other in a receptive gesture.

Every line drawn is like a line drawn on water. One who draws it has a judgmental satisfaction, but in reality, there is no line drawn. Rather, it is like the sun that shines equally on everybody, bringing warmth and light. People do stumble. That is the test of the others' patience and compassion. Sometimes people do go wrong. There is no judgment for it. Wrong will take a short or long time to make the individual aware that wrong is wrong, and that is the beginning of awakening. Punishment is not the human way of life. Faults and shortcomings are caused by ignorance. Compassion and patience pay. Let's pray all will be great tomorrow.

Concluding a Set and Your Session

After a deep relaxation following a kriya or meditation, the exercises below will help to ground you. You may add to these exercises.

1. On your back, begin rotating your feet and hands in small circles. Continue in one direction for 30 seconds, then in the other direction for another 30 seconds.

2. Cat Stretch: Keeping both shoulders and the left leg flat on the ground, bring the right arm back behind the head and the right knee over the left leg until it touches the floor on the far side of the body. Switch legs and arms and repeat the exercise. This stretch can be done with both legs to the same side.

3. Still on your back, bring the knees up and to the sides and rub the soles of the feet and the palms of the hands together briskly, creating a sensation of heat for 1 minute.

4. Clasping knees to chest with both hands, begin rolling back and forth on the spine. Roll all the way back until the feet touch the ground behind the head and all the way forward until you're sitting up. Do this 3-4 times at least.

5. Sit up in Easy Pose. Contain your energy by feeling centered inside your space, inside your skin. Be with the flow of your breath. Enjoy your feeling presence.

6. Enjoy a meditation of your choice.

7. To end your session, bring your palms together in Prayer Mudra at the heart center. End by singing or repeating as a prayer: **"May the long time Sun shine upon you, all love surround you, and the pure light within you, guide your way on."**

8. Inhale and say a prayer of thanks. Exhale and release a thought of gratitude into the Universe.

Wake Up Series

Yogi Bhajan recommended doing the following series every morning upon (or even before) arising. The exercises can be done while still in bed.

1. Stretch Pose: Lying on back, raise head and feet 6 inches off the ground and hold with Breath of Fire for 30 seconds to 2 minutes, or as long as possible. Eyes look at big toes. Hands face inward and point toward feet. If the small of the back comes up, place hands beneath hips for support. (Pulling the shoulders toward the head puts excessive strain on the neck muscles. Keeping the diaphragm and chest lifted takes pressure off the neck. To avoid engaging the neck muscles, strengthen the abdominal muscles first with simpler exercises.) If held less than a minute, rest and repeat pose, increasing time as core muscles strengthen. Sets the navel and builds core strength.

2. Nose to Knees: Bend the knees and clasp legs with arms, raising head so that nose comes between knees, and hold position with Breath of Fire for 2 minutes. Combines prana with apana and eliminates intestinal gas.

3. Spinal Rock: In same position, rock back and forth on the spine from neck to tailbone for 1 minute. Distributes pranic energy and relaxes spine.

4. Ego Eradicator: Sit in Easy Pose and raise arms 60 degrees out to the sides, fingertips on pads of fingers, thumbs extended straight up, and hold with Breath of Fire for 2 minutes. Deeply inhale, then slowly raise arms until thumb tips touch overhead. Flatten hands, palms facing outward, and slowly arc them down, sweeping the aura with the palms, clearing any darkness, negativity, or sickness. Release into the Earth to clean and energize the aura. Feel light and clarity around you and meditate on that light.

Warm Up Exercise Set

1. Spinal Flexes on heels: Sitting on heels with hands resting on knees, flex the spine back and forth, inhaling as it arches forward and up slightly, exhaling as it contracts back, for 1-3 minutes.

2. Spinal Twists: Sitting on heels with hands on shoulders, fingers in front and thumbs in back, inhale as you twist your torso to the left, exhale as you twist right, for 1-3 minutes.

3. Shoulder Shrugs: Relax hands down on knees and inhale while raising shoulders to ears; exhale relaxing them down again. Repeat for 1-3 minutes.

4. Neck Rolls: Pull up on the spine from the back of the neck so that the head rests on top of the spine. From a forward position, circle head to the right, then gently back, then to the left, and then forward again. Continue making slow, smooth circles, ironing out any kinks as you go, and reverse directions, for 1-2 minutes each direction.

5. Cat-Cow: On hands and knees, with thighs directly under hips, arms directly under shoulders, thighs and arms parallel to each other, arch the back up with the exhale, lowering the head to the chest. On the inhale, press the tummy toward the floor as the neck arches back, and continue, increasing speed as you go for 1-3 minutes.

6. Life-Nerve Stretches:
   a. With both legs stretched out in front, feet flat to get a good stretch of the sciatic nerve from the heels to the hip, bend from the hips and grab toes or wherever you can, keeping the knees on the floor and the legs straight. As you exhale, pull the chest toward the knees, keeping a straight spine and open heart. On the inhale, come up. Stretch, do not strain, for 1-2 minutes.
   b. Next, place the left heel in the inner right thigh near groin. Inhale up, stretch your spine. Bending from hips with a straight spine, grab your toes, if you can, or any other point on your leg that allows you to keep your leg straight. Hold with Breath of Fire for 1-2 minutes. To end, inhale, hold the breath, and apply the locks. Switch legs and repeat.

7. Spread legs wide apart, grabbing onto toes or your legs. Inhale up to center, exhale and bend from hips, aiming chest toward your left leg. Inhale center, exhale toward the right leg, inhale center, and repeat on alternate legs for 1-2 minutes. Stretch your spine. Do not bend spine at heart area to try to get your head to your knee.

8. Stretch Pose: Lying on back, arms and legs kept straight, raise feet, head, and hands 6 inches off the ground and hold with Breath of Fire for one minute or as long as possible. Eyes should look at big toes and hands point toward feet. If the waist comes up, place hands beneath hips for support. If held less than a minute, rest and repeat pose, increasing time daily. Sets the navel.

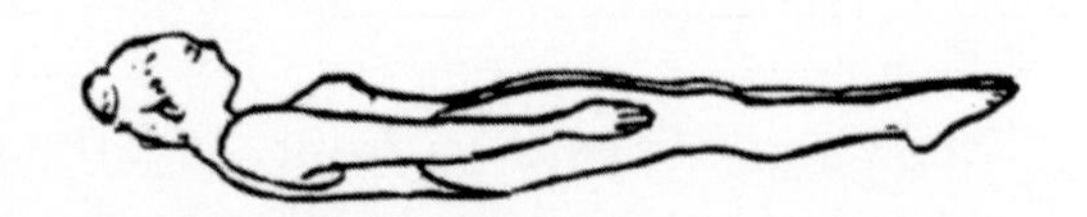

9. Relax on your back.

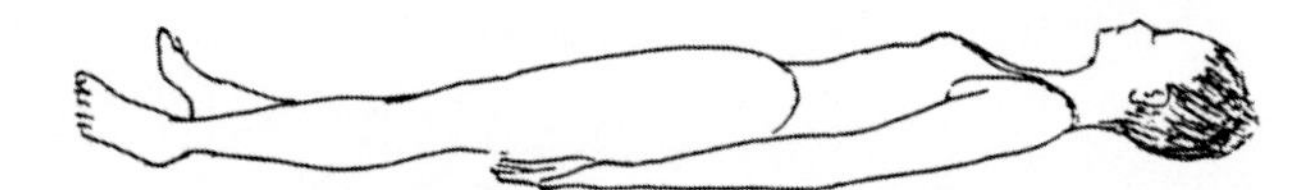

> There are a lot of things that you think you can't do, like looking unique or being excellent. But you only think these things because you are afraid of the responsibility. If the psyche is corrected once in awhile, for a few minutes here, or a few minutes there, you'll be surprised how much good you can do for yourself.

Nabhi Kriya

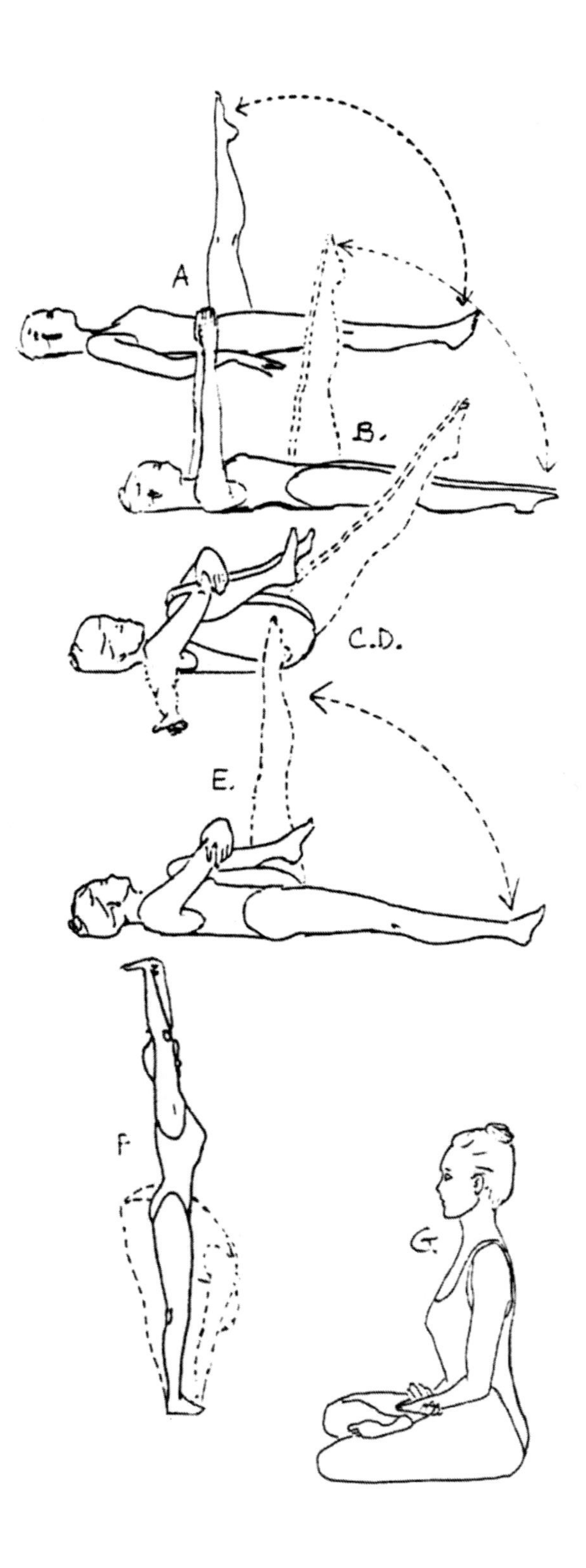

A. On back, inhale and lift right leg up to 90 degrees, exhale and lower it. Repeat with left leg. Continue alternate leg lifts with deep, powerful breathing for 1 minute or 26 times (building up to 10 minutes). Relax and feel the pulse at your navel.

B. Still on your back, arms stretched straight up from the heart, palms facing each other, lift both legs up to 90 degrees on the inhale and lower them on the exhale. Start out with one leg at a time to develop abdominal muscles. Moves energy from navel to heart. 1 minute or 26 times (up to 5 minutes).

C. Bend knees and clasp them to chest with the arms, allowing the head to relax back. Rest in this position for 5 minutes.

D. In #C position above, inhale, open the arms straight out to the sides on the ground, and extend the legs straight out to 60 degrees. Exhale and return to the original position. Repeat and continue for 1 minute or 26 times (up to 15 minutes). (#C & #D are Pavan Sodan Kriya).

E. On back, bring left knee to the chest, hold it there with both hands, and rapidly raise and lower the right leg to 90 degrees, inhaling up, exhaling down, for 1 minute or 26 times. Switch legs and repeat for 1 minute or 26 times. Repeat the complete cycle once more.

F. Stand up straight, raising arms overhead, hugging ears. Press fingers back so that palms face sky/ceiling. Exhale as you bend forward to touch the ground, keeping the arms straight and hugging ears. Then inhale up very slowly with deep breath. On exhale, apply root lock. Bend from the hips. Continue at a slow pace for 2 minutes or 26 times, then more rapidly for 1 more minute.

G. Totally relax or meditate for 10-15 minutes.

COMMENTS: One of the most popular Kundalini Yoga kriyas, this set focuses on developing core strength at the navel center. Times indicated are for advanced students. To begin practice, start with 1 minute on the longer exercises. Exercise #A is for the lower digestive area; #B is for upper digestion and solar plexus; #C eliminates gas and relaxes the heart; #D charges the magnetic field and opens the navel center; #E opens the hips and lower spine; #F is for entire spine, spinal fluid, the aura, and grounding. This set gets the abdominal area in shape quickly.

Also, note #D is a very powerful exercise that can be included in warm ups. As you extend the arms and the legs, be aware that the stretch is aligning the central channel in the front of the body from the pubic bone up to the heart. This exercise can also be done by bringing the arms above the head, setting the front channel from the public bone to the collarbone. Both positions create a state of emotional balance.

Energy & Relaxation for Nerves

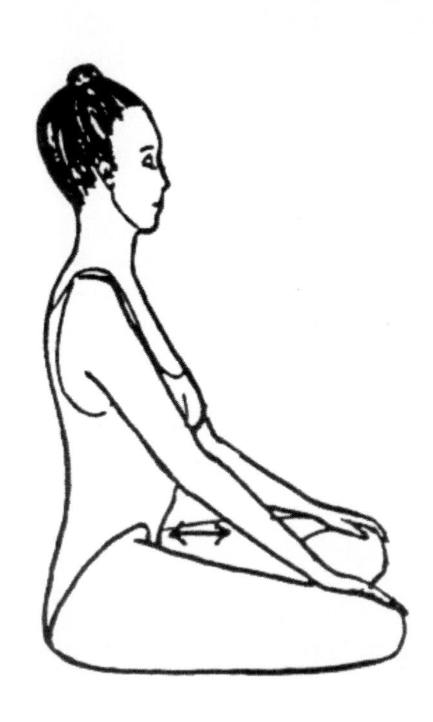

In Easy Pose, inhale, hold, pull and release root lock 3 times. Then exhale, and while suspending the breath, pull and release all the locks, including diaphragm lock. (With the breath held out, it is possible to apply the diaphragm lock.) Do this sequence for 1-3 minutes. Then extend your legs in front of you and give them a good stretch.

Now inhale, exhale, hold the breath out and pull and relax mahabhand (all the locks) 3 times; inhale and repeat for 1-3 minutes. Relax the legs, stretching them out.

As you pull the locks, focus your attention on the spine. Feel the aliveness and increased awareness.

Follow these exercises with a few minutes of simply being aware of subtle energies in your spine and body. Allow these higher energies to replace any negativity. Let go, if only for an instant, so the release can happen. You are not in charge of the release, but you must let go to allow it to happen.

COMMENTS: This is a simple kriya that can be done alone or added to your daily practice. It helps you learn how to use the locks and to cultivate inner consciousness and subtle sensitivity. Do this exercise for 40 days to release negativity and to activate the pure flow of Kundalini energy in your spine. Do it with awareness and pay attention to the subtle sensations in your spine and body.

Spinal Energy Series

During each exercise, mentally vibrate SAT on the inhale and NAM on the exhale. At the end of each exercise, inhale deeply and suspend the breath while relaxing the body. Pull mahabhand, allowing the energy to move from the base of the spine up to the third eye. Exhale. Then inhale and exhale and pull mahabhand again while suspending the breath, holding out the exhale. Inhale. Relax and be aware of the sensations in your spine. Cultivate consciousness for 1-2 minutes between each exercise.

1. Spinal Flexes in Easy Pose: In Easy Pose, grab on to your ankles and slightly pull on them as you flex the spine forward and pull up on the spine. As you exhale, relax the spine backwards. On each inhale, lightly pull up on the spine from the back of the neck to elongate the spine. This works on the lower spine. The head does not bob up and down with the movement. 1-2 minutes or 26 to 108 times.

2. Spinal Flexes on Knees: Sitting on your heels, rest the hands on the thighs. Flex the spine forward on the inhale and back on the exhale. This works on the mid spine.

3. Spinal Twists: Place the hands on the shoulders, fingers in front, thumbs in back. Inhale as you twist left, exhale as you twist right. To end, inhale forward. 1-2 minutes or 26 times.

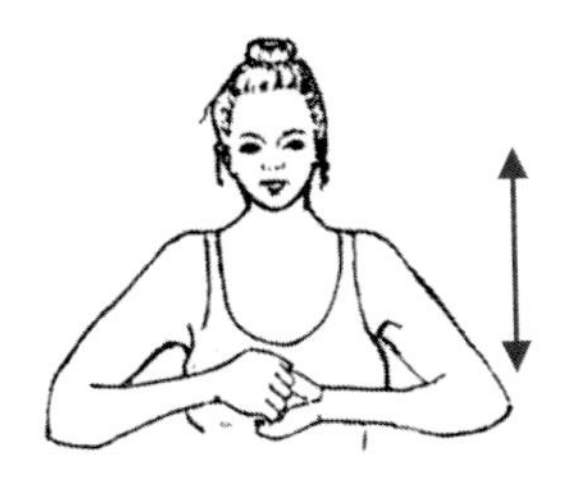

4. See-Saw: Lock the hands in Bear Grip (fingers of both hands hooked together, left palm facing out) at the heart center. With a powerful breath, inhale and exhale as you move alternate elbows up and down like a see-saw. 1-2 minutes or 26 times. To end, inhale, hold, pull on the hands while the arms are parallel to the ground, pull the locks. Exhale, inhale, exhale, pull on hands again and pull the locks.

5. Spinal Flexes in Easy Pose: This time grab the knees, keeping the elbows straight. Inhale, flex the upper spine forward and exhale back. With the elbows straight, you will only flex the upper spine. 1-2 minutes or 26 times.

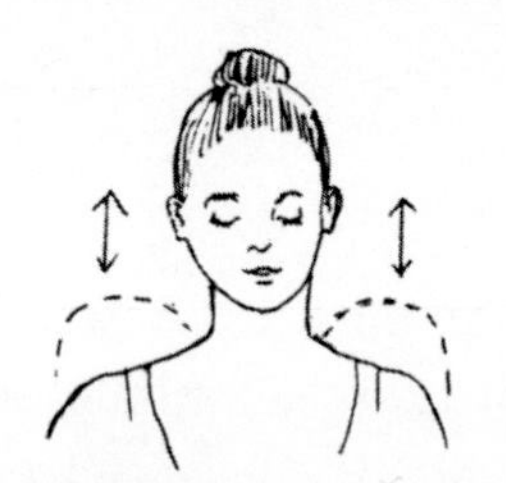

6. Shoulder Shrugs: Shrug the shoulders up on the inhale and move down gently (do not slam down) on the exhale. Focus on the upper spine. Release tension in the shoulders. 1 minute.

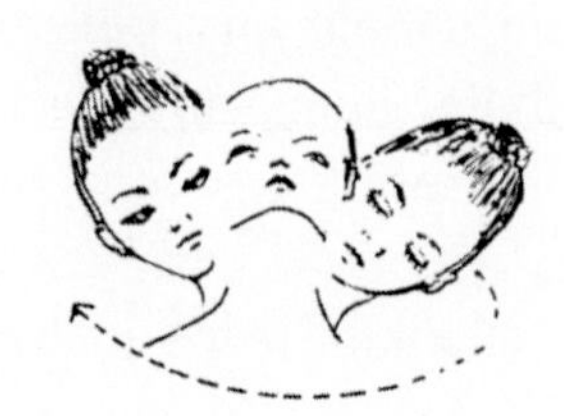

7. Neck Rolls: Before doing neck rolls, pull up on the spine from the back of the neck to make sure that your head feels like it is floating on top of your spine. You can also move the head from left to right a couple of times. Slowly move the head in a circle to the left a few times and then to the right. Be sure to breathe long and deep while moving the head.

8. Bear Grip: Lock the hands in Bear Grip at the level of the throat. Pulling on the hands, inhale and apply the root lock, then exhale and apply the root lock. Feel the energy from the base of the spine to the throat. Then raise the hands in Bear Grip above the head. Holding the position and pulling on the hands, inhale, apply the root lock, and then exhale and apply the root lock. Feel the energy move from the base of the spine up to the top of the head.

   Repeat the above cycle (hands at throat and then above the head) a total of 3 times.

9. Do Sat Kriya for 3-5 minutes (see next page for instructions).

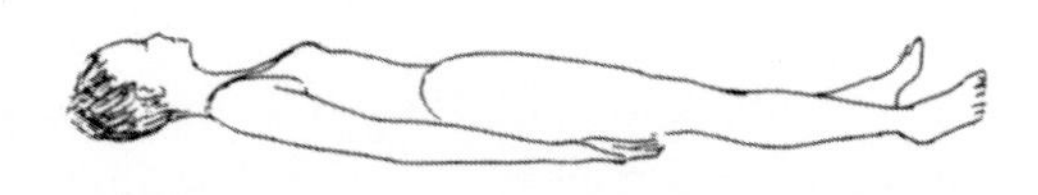

10. Deep Relaxation: Relax on your back for 10 minutes or up to 15 depending on how long you have done Sat Kriya.

COMMENTS: This basic set works on the flexibility of the spine and general spinal health. With the application of the locks, it awakens the channels in the spine so that the Kundalini can rise. This kriya starts at the base of the spine and works up the spine activating all the chakras.

> The best justice is to avoid negative environments and to act with non-violence so that you can enjoy life and create environments for others to enjoy.

Sat Kriya

Sat Kriya is fundamental to Kundalini Yoga and is one of the most effective kriyas to repair and reverse the damage done to our system from from stress and taking drugs. It is recommended to include at least 3 minutes of Sat Kriya in our daily practice for these and other benefits:

- Sat Kriya helps heal sexual dysfunctions (including impotency, premature ejaculation, and sexual phobias) by strengthening the entire sexual system and by stimulating the natural flow of sexual energy. It balances sexual impulses by channeling sexual energy into our body systems and making this valuable creative force available for all our creative activities.
- People suffering from mental and emotional disorders can benefit from practicing Sat Kriya because it balances and channels the unbalanced and misdirected energy in the lower three chakras.
- We can improve our general physical heath and strengthen our heart through the distribution of sexual energy and the rhythmic movement this exercise provides.
- Sat Kriya activates and channels Kundalini energy to nurture our whole system and awaken our consciousness.

Directions for Sat Kriya

Sit on the heels and stretch arms overhead, elbows hugging ears, fingers interlocked, index fingers extended straight up.

Chant SAT NAM in a constant rhythm of about 8 times per 10 seconds or at a pace that you find comfortable, being careful not to speed up. Chant from the navel and solar plexus, pulling the umbilicus into the spine on SAT and relaxing the belly on NAM. ("Sat Nam" rhymes with "but mom"). This creates a wave-like motion in the spine, with SAT creating a wave up the spine, and NAM allowing a wave down the spine.

Focus on pulling the navel point in, but do not try to consciously apply root lock. The lock will occur naturally as the muscles used to pull in the navel are connected to the other muscles used in the root lock. The hips and spine do not flex, as the only motion is a slight up and down movement of the chest and arms with each SAT NAM.

To end, inhale deeply, suspend the breath, and lightly apply the locks, using the muscles from the anus, sex organ, perineum, diaphragm, and neck to allow the energy to flow up the spine and out through the top of the head. Exhale powerfully. Inhale deeply, exhale, hold the breath out, and apply the locks. The locks on the suspended breath can be done several times. Do the locks suspending the breath on both the inhale and the exhale to balance and mix prana and apana.

If you have not taken drugs or have cleared your system of all their effects, you may choose to practice the kriya with the palms open, pressing against each other. This releases more energy but is not generally taught in a public class because someone may have weak nerves from drug abuse. It is also harder to maintain the position when the hands are not interlaced.

Continue for at least 3 minutes. Time may be built to 31 minutes, but 5-11 minutes is good.

One way to build duration is to start with 2-3 minutes and rest for 3-5 minutes and then repeat 2-3 minutes practice, 3-5 minutes rest. Or simply increase by one minute a day, or as you feel appropriate for yourself.

Always end with a long deep relaxation immediately afterwards. The longer you practice Sat Kriya, the longer you need to relax to allow the integration of the energy. Never jump right up after practicing this kriya. Give your body the time it needs to integrate the effects. You want to ground in the benefits.

COMMENTS: The classic Sat Kriya can be done by itself or added at the end of warm up exercises or at the end of a set. Sat Kriya pumps sexual energy throughout our whole system and up to our brain and raises the Kundalini. Respect the power of this technology and allow this kriya to heal your body and to properly prepare your body for higher experiences. This is not just an exercise — it is a kriya that works on all levels of being, known and unknown, conscious, unconscious, and subconscious.

Sat Kriya activates subtle energies. This is not an aerobic sport. You can block the flow of energy and miss the subtle experiences of higher energies by pushing the physical body too much and being too aggressive in your practice. Or with too much stimulation, you could have a rush of energy or a fleeting pranic experience, but be unable to integrate it into your psyche. So prepare yourself with constancy, patience, and moderation. Transformation is assured. If you have time for nothing else, practice this kriya daily to keep your body a clean and vital temple for your soul!

Sat Kriya Video

Guru Rattana shares how to do Sat Kriya in a subtle, internal, and most impactful way in a free video, available on YouTube (https://www.youtube.com/watch?v=gK118KEGWKc). She explains how to use the small muscles involved in the internal locks to adjust the spine and increase the flow of energy up and down the spine. This delicate approach enhances the energy released in the lower chakras and awakens the light in the third eye. The subtle stimulation created by the muscle movements, combined with the sound current of SAT NAM, create an awakening of consciousness.

Kriya for Elevation

This easy set is a tune up for the spine and the chakras.

1. Ego Eradicator: In Easy Pose, raise the arms up to 60 degrees with the thumbs pointing straight up in the air like antennae. Fingers are curled into the pads of the palms. Eyes are closed. Be aware of the energy between your arms, which is the arc line. Build the arc line or light around your head with Breath of Fire for 1-3 minutes.

   To end, inhale deeply, hold the breath as you slowly (with concentration) bring the thumb tips together. When the thumbs touch, slowly exhale as you bring the hands down, palms facing down, through the aura, clearing the aura. Press any negativity or darkness into the ground with the palms. Sit and feel the light around your body and head.

2. Spinal Flex: In Easy Pose, hold on to the ankles with the hands. Lightly pull on the ankles to stimulate the spine as you inhale forward and exhale back. Keep the shoulders relaxed and the head straight. (Do not bob the head up and down.) Continue rhythmically with powerful breathing for 1-3 minutes. To end, inhale deeply, suspend the breath, apply the locks. Exhale powerfully, inhale deeply, exhale, and apply the locks on the suspended exhale.

3. Spinal Twist: In Easy Pose, hold on to the shoulders with the fingers in front and the thumbs in back. Keep the elbows parallel to the ground, slightly pressed back to open the heart. Inhale as you twist the torso, shoulders, and head to the left, and exhale as you twist right. Continue 1-3 minutes. To end, inhale deeply, suspend the breath, pull the locks. Exhale powerfully, inhale deeply, exhale, and apply the locks on the suspended exhale.

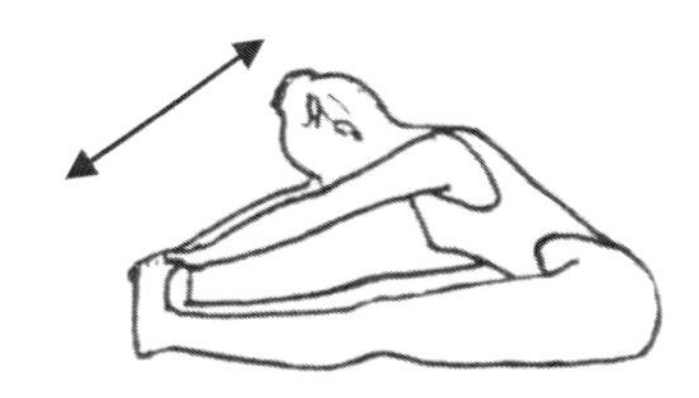

4. Life-Nerve Stretch: With both legs stretched out in front, grab on to the big toes, pressurizing both the nail and the fleshy backside with the thumb and forefinger. Inhale as you pull up on the spine. Exhale as you stretch from the hips to bring the chest forward (heart open) toward the legs. Stretch both the spine and the legs on both the upward and downward movements. Continue with powerful breathing for 1-3 minutes. To end, inhale up, suspend the breath, and apply the locks. Exhale and apply the locks.

5. Alternate Leg Stretches: Left leg is extended forward. Right leg is bent at the knee, bringing the heel under the buttocks (if you can). Bend forward from the hips, keeping the spine straight. Grab the big toe of the left foot with the thumb and forefinger of both hands. Pressurize the toe's nail and the fleshy backside. Inhale up to stretch the spine. Then stretch forward on a slow exhale. Come down as far as you are able while maintaining a straight spine and an open heart. Do long deep breathing or Breath of Fire for 1-2 minutes. To end, inhale deeply, as you exhale stretch a bit more. Repeat on the other side. .

6. Wide Life-Nerve Stretch: With the legs spread wide apart, grab on to the toes if possible (or grab on to where you can). Inhale as you stretch up straight, pulling up on the toes. On the exhale, bend from the hips, keeping a straight spine, and bring the heart toward the left knee. Inhale up and bend toward the right knee. Absolutely do not bend at the heart to try to get your head to your knee. Stretch the elongated spine and legs with each slow movement on a long inhale and exhale. Continue for 1-2 minutes. Then inhale up to the center and exhale as you pull the spine from the hips toward the center. Continue for 1 minute. Make a longer stretch on both the inhale and exhale to end.

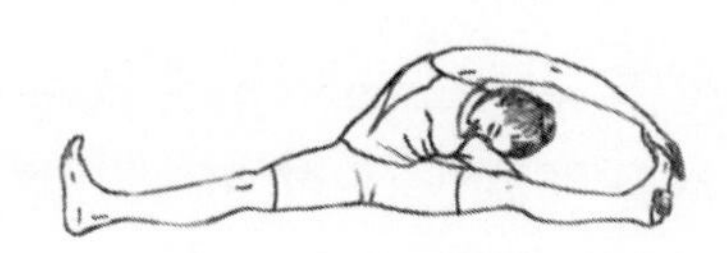

7. Cobra Pose: On the stomach with the palms on the floor under the shoulders, inhale as you arch the spine up slowly vertebra by vertebra, until the arms are almost straight but elbows are slightly bent. The pelvis does not come off the ground. Slowly go up and down several times until your spine is relaxed and you can easily hold the posture. Then hold in the up position with Breath of Fire for 1-3 minutes. To end, inhale deeply, stretch the spine, exhale, and apply the root lock. Inhale deeply and then slowly exhale as you come down very slowly one vertebra at a time. Relax on your stomach and let go of stress in the back, shoulders, and face.

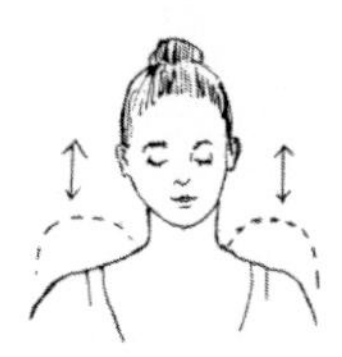

8. Shoulder Shrugs: In Easy Pose with the hands on the knees, inhale deeply as you bring the shoulders toward the ears. Exhale and gently allow the shoulders to relax down. Continue rhythmically for 1-2 minutes.

9. Neck Rolls: In Easy Pose, pull up on the diaphragm and elongate the spine until the head relaxes on top of the spine. Slowly move the head in one direction for 1-2 minutes, gently stretching and moving through any tightness. Then change directions for 1-2 minutes.

10. Do Sat Kriya for 3-7 minutes. (See page 103.)

11. Relax on the back with the arms to the sides, palms facing up. Enjoy letting go and feeling more alive.

Guru Rattana's Set for Strengthening Circulation, the Heart, & Immune System

The following exercises stimulate and balance the whole body. They can be done individually or as a set to give you a quick pickup.

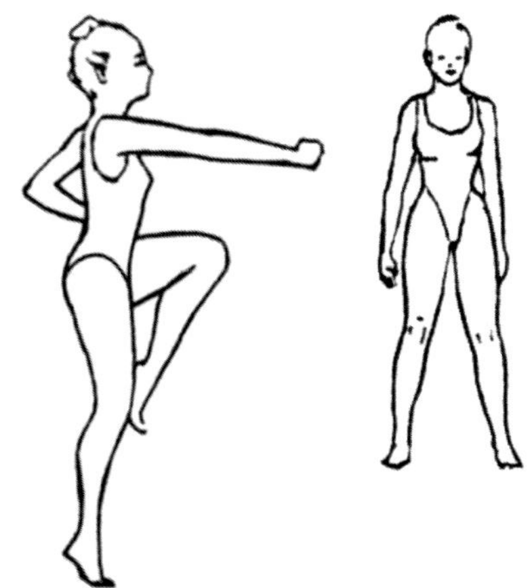

1. Running in Place: Run in place raising the knees and punching the fists alternately, using a powerful breath with each punch. Bring the knees up as far as possible and really go for it. To end, inhale, exhale, and stand perfectly still, letting the energy circulate and the breath relax — feel centered at the navel and focus at the third eye. This jogging substitute will get your energy going if done vigorously. It is great to do on a mini-trampoline, which absorbs shock. 1-5 minutes or up to 20 minutes if done by itself.

2. Cross-crawls: Standing, raise the left leg to the chest while raising the right arm straight up. Then alternate arms and legs. Coordinate with a powerful breath for 1-3 minutes. Then lying on the back, raise the left leg 90 degrees, with the right arm overhead on the floor. Alternate with right leg and left arm. Breathe powerfully.

   Cross-crawls establish balance in the right and left hemispheres of the brain and strengthen the electromagnetic field. Carrying things weakens us. Walking with arms swinging at the sides keeps our energy balanced and strength intact.

   (Studies show that people laden with packages are particularly vulnerable to assault. The weakened electromagnetic field contributes to the phenomenon.)

3. Frog Pose: Squat, with buttocks resting on heels, knees spread apart, toes wide, heels together and raised, arms between knees, fingertips on the floor, head up and facing straight ahead. Inhale, raise the buttocks high, keeping fingertips on the ground and heels together and raised throughout. At the height of inhalation, the head is down, facing the knees. Exhale and return to the original position, coming down so that the buttocks strike the heels.

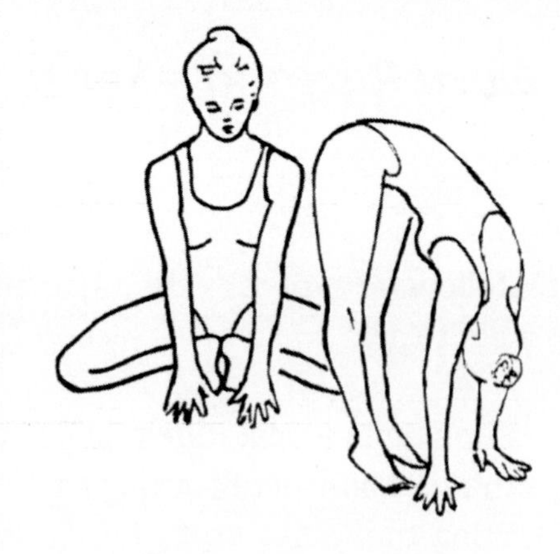

Frog Pose can be done 26, 52, or 108 times. (Actually it can be done as long as you can or would like to do it.) This is a good physical workout. It stimulates and circulates sexual energy and helps maintain potency. You will definitely be able to sleep if you do this before going to bed. Be sure to do it on an empty stomach. Do it 5 minutes a day for unbounded energy and a positive mind. (You may not feel positive during the exercise, though!)

4. Leg Stretches: Legs out in front, grab knees, ankles, or toes, whichever you can comfortably. Keep knees on the floor. Inhale up, exhale down, for 1-3 minutes. (If you can't reach your toes, you can use a towel, sock, necktie, etc., to place around the toes and hold on to it.) If you can, grab the toes and squeeze the big toenail against the fleshy part to stimulate the pituitary.

5. Spinal Twists: Sitting in a comfortable cross-legged position or in Rock Pose, hands on shoulders (fingers in front, thumbs back), twist the upper torso from side to side, inhaling as the left elbow goes back, exhaling as the right goes back, for 1-3 minutes. Keep arms parallel to the ground. This opens the heart center.

6 Heart-Strengthening Exercise: In Easy Pose with a straight spine and eyes closed, raise the arms up to a 60 degree angle, keeping the elbows straight with the palms facing up, fingers together. Begin breathing long and deep through the nose, or do a powerful Breath of Fire for a minimum of 1 minute to a maximum of 3 minutes. (At minimum, add 20 seconds a day until you reach maximum.) To end, inhale deeply, hold the breath for 10 seconds, then exhale and relax, resting the hands in the lap. Remain seated for another minute, eyes closed, feeling the calming effect of the pose.

Exercise Tips: If some of your thoughts tell you to lower the arms before you should, let the thoughts come and go, but *keep the arms in position* to experience the effect of this pose. The arms may shake slightly from the release of built up tension. Any tingling is caused by increased nerve activity. Concentrate on your breathing and keep the elbows straight (the two keys to the exercise). The more you do this exercise, the easier and more beneficial and enjoyable it becomes.

This exercise relaxes the heart and stimulates the nerves that go from the fingertips, through the hands and arms, and into the chest, meeting at the heart center. Holding the position properly for 2-3 minutes relaxes the heart muscle, expands the lungs, and cleans the entire upper torso through the stimulation of the lymph system. Shoulder and neck muscles are in an isometric flex, and a wave of relaxation flows into them afterwards. This exercise makes you feel light and at ease, as tension is released from the upper body.

7. Relax in Easy Pose or on the back for 5 minutes.

8. Meditate from the heart or pick any of the heart meditations that you enjoy.

Kriya for Physical & Mental Vitality

1. Lie on the back, lift legs 12 inches, and begin crisscrossing left over right, right over left, spreading legs as wide as is comfortable. Keep legs straight. Be sure to apply root lock and use your abdominal muscles. Place hands under hips to keep small of the back flat on the ground. Start with 30 seconds and work up to 2-3 minutes. Before coming down, apply root lock and pull in navel. Rest 2-3 minutes and repeat the cycle.

2. Lift both legs 2 feet and begin a push-pull motion with knees bent, moving from hips. Keep lower legs parallel to the ground. Continue for 1 to 2 minutes. Rest 2 minutes and repeat cycle. Exercises 1 and 2 activate the navel center and move the Kundalini energy from the lower three chakras.

3. Seated in Easy Pose, lift the arms straight above the head, fingers interlocked, palms facing up. Do Breath of Fire for 2-5 minutes. To end, inhale deeply, suspend the breath, pull root lock, and focus at the heart center. This moves the energy from the lower chakras to the upper chakras and to the heart center.

   Sit quietly afterwards with hands on knees. Feel all the worries of the day drop away. Your aura and entire body are filled with light and prana. Enjoy the lightness and your breath.

4. Clasp opposite shoulders, arms behind the head, thumbs forward. Hold this posture with Breath of Fire for 2-5 minutes. To end, holding the position, (1) inhale powerfully, exhale powerfully, then inhale deeply and hold the breath as you relax your body and allow the energy to circulate. (2) Exhale, hold, apply root lock, and allow the energy to circulate. Repeat a total of 2 times.

   Sit quietly and enjoy the clear open, peaceful space in your head, heart, whole body, and around your body.

5. After meditating, relax completely on your back, enjoying aliveness, flow, and an expansive space.

6. Sitting in Easy Pose, chant any divine mantra for 2-11 minutes.

COMMENTS: This is a good kriya to do when you need a short set that balances and integrates both the upper and lower chakras. This set brings you into a state of wholeness. It is the perfect set for when you don't think that you have time to do yoga. You will feel revitalized, relaxed, and ready to go for the day. Work up to longer times. Be sure to relax and integrate between exercises and after the set.

> Don't think that if there is a challenge in your life, then you have no life. Life without challenge doesn't exist. Challenge is that which is answered by you, and your answer is by your qualification. So you have to qualify yourself to be up to the challenge.

To Remove Negativity

This short set helps relieve negativity, depression, anger, and fatigue. It also releases stress in the back, neck, and shoulders. This combination is great to do at the end of the day before dinner or before going to bed.

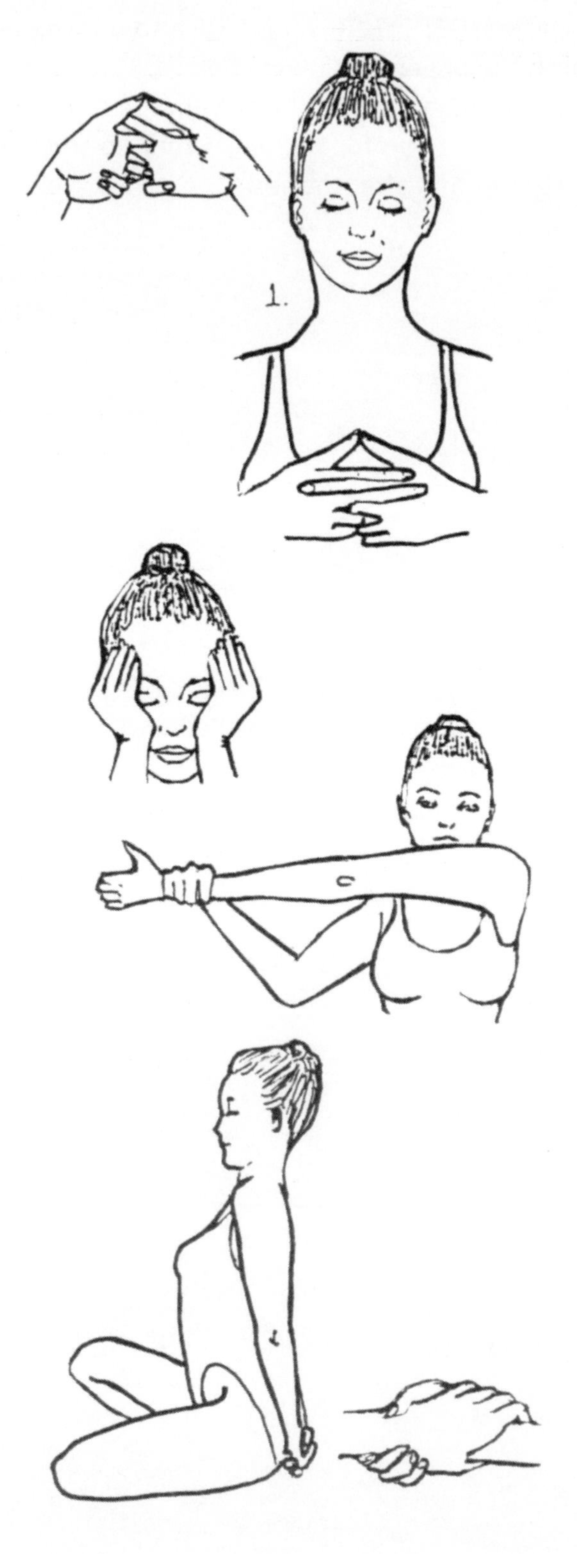

1. Clasp fingers in Venus Lock, but curl Mercury (little) and Sun (ring) fingers into the palms instead of crossing them. Then hook left Saturn (middle) finger over right Sun (ring) finger and pull hard. Focus at the third eye, continuously pulling hard on the finger lock for 1-3 minutes with long deep breathing. Removes anger and enthrones the neutral mind.

2. Place the base of the palms under the cheekbones and push as hard as you can for 1-3 minutes. It doesn't have to hurt, but if it does, you have the right spot. Makes you feel happy! (afterwards)

3. Grasp left wrist with the right hand and pull the left arm as far to the right as possible (and then some more!) for 1-3 minutes. Repeat on other side. Be sure to keep the head forward and do not twist the body. Removes tension across the shoulder blades.

4. Clasp the wrists with your hands behind the back and with the hands touching the spine, try to bring elbows together. Pull on arms as you arch the chest out and apply chin lock for 1-3 minutes. Raises energy up the spine and elevates you!

5. Standing up, shake every part of your body. Let go of stress and old energy from the day.

6. Deeply relax on your back.

COMMENTS: This short set leaves you feeling great!

Basic Breath Series

1. Sit in Easy Pose. Make an antenna of the right hand's fingers and block the right nostril with the thumb. Begin long deep breathing through the left nostril for 3 minutes. Inhale and hold for 10 seconds.

2. Repeat the first exercise, but use the left hand and breathe through the right nostril. Continue for 3 minutes. Inhale and hold for 10 seconds.

3. Using the thumb and the little finger to close alternate nostrils, inhale through the left nostril and exhale through the right with long deep breaths for 3 minutes.

4. Repeat exercise 3, except inhale through the right nostril and exhale through the left.

5. Sit in Easy Pose with hands on knees in Gyan Mudra, thumbs and forefingers touching, elbows straight. Begin Breath of Fire. Totally center yourself at the brow point. Continue with powerful Breath of Fire for 2 to 7½ minutes. Then inhale, circulating the energy. Relax or meditate for 5 minutes, then chant long SAT NAMs for at least 3 minutes, but for up to 11 minutes if you want.

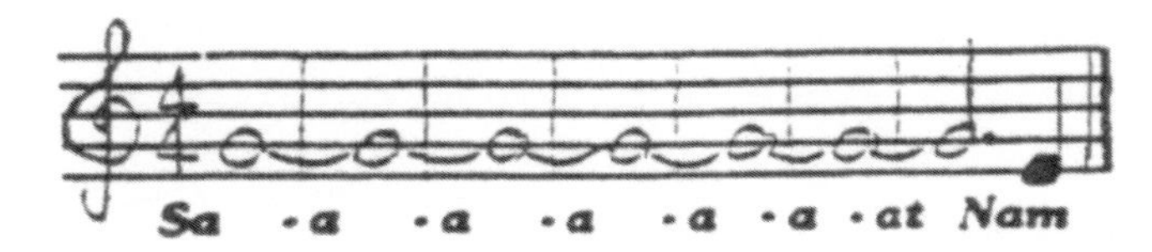

COMMENTS: This set opens the pranic channels and balances the breath in the two sides of your body. It is often practiced before a more strenuous, physical exercise. It is great to do by itself whenever you need a quick lift and a clear mind. It strengthens the nervous system, energizes, calms, and balances.

Pranayama Series to Balance Prana and Apana

1. In Easy Pose, arms straight out to sides parallel to ground, palms up, do Breath of Fire for 1-3 minutes. To end: inhale, turn palms over and press them out, hold, and exhale.

2. To bring in Sun energy: Place upper arms parallel to the ground, forearms up, palms forward, thumbs and ring finger touching in Surya Mudra. Inhale in four parts, and exhale in four parts, pumping the navel for 1-3 minutes. To end: inhale, bring palms together, pull root lock, stretch palms up, and exhale down.

3. To balance the vertical and horizontal auras:

   A. Interlace fingers, arms out in front parallel to the ground, palms facing out. Inhale and lift hands overhead, exhale and bring them down in front. Repeat and continue for 1-3 minutes. Then inhale and bring hands down to the sides.

   B. With arms out to sides parallel to the ground, palms out, inhale and bring backs of hands together overhead; exhale down to parallel again. Repeat and continue for 1-3 minutes.

4. With upper arms out to sides, parallel to ground, forearms up to 90 degrees, thumb and index fingers touching in Gyan Mudra, inhale and twist torso left, exhale and twist right. Continue for 1-3 minutes.

5. With hands on shoulders, thumbs in back, fingers in front, bend side to side, inhaling left, exhaling right, allowing head and neck to relax. Repeat and continue for 2-3 minutes.

6. Alternate Nostril Breathing. Closing right nostril with right thumb and left nostril with right ring finger, quickly inhale through left nostril and exhale through right for 2-3 minutes.

7. Sitali Pranayam: Curl the tongue and stick it out, inhaling through the curled tongue and exhaling through the nose, with chin lock pulled. Continue for 3-5 minutes.

8. With hands at heart center, first three fingers are touching each other and opposite fingertips. Thumbs and little fingers are pulled apart but touching opposite thumb/fingertips. Look through the fingers at the little fingers and inhale through the nose, exhale through mouth, then inhale through the mouth and exhale through the nose. Repeat and continue sequence for 2-5 minutes.

COMMENTS: This simple pranayama series, with upper arm moving postures and meditative breathing, can change your life. It can be done in a chair, wheelchair, or in bed. This set is for everyone! You can pick just one or two exercises if you wish and enjoy the rejuvenating power of your breath.

Following each exercise, suspend your breath. Use the suspended space to expand your awareness of your inner reality and to enjoy the richness of being alive. For maximum results, between each exercise suspend your breath on the inhale and then on the exhale: inhale deeply, suspend, exhale, inhale, exhale, suspend. To release addictions, after the final exercise, inhale deeply, suspend the breath, exhale, and repeat 7-15 to times. Connect with the purity within and let the light of your soul release any addictive urges. The oxygenation of the blood will bring you into a state of freedom and peace. The will of your soul is in charge, not the will of the addiction. Enjoy the high you feel in this deep and pure space.

Heart of Gold

1. Yoga Mudra: In Lotus (or Easy) Pose, bend over placing forehead on the ground, hands in Venus Lock behind the back, index fingers extended, and raise the arms straight up, pulling the shoulder blades together with long deep breathing for 3 minutes.

2. In Easy Pose, lean forward to 60 degrees, grasp opposite shoulder blades, pulling right arm under left, and hold with long deep breathing for 3 minutes.

3. With arms stretched straight out in front, parallel to the ground, spread the fingers wide apart, feeling heat at the base of the palms, and hold with long deep breathing for 3 minutes. Then tense hands and relax. Brings energy to the heart in two shifts.

4. Rub hands in a circular motion around the centers of the palms for 3 minutes.

5. With upper arms at sides, bring left one out to the side away from the body and hold the right one close in, palms facing each other, and meditate on the energy between the hands for 7-15 minutes.

6. Ego Eradicator: With arms up to the sides at 60 degrees, fingertips on pads and thumbs extended up, breathe long and deep for 1-2 minutes, and then follow with 1-2 minutes of Breath of Fire.

7. Repeat #4.

8. Place palms 4-6 inches apart at the heart center, palms facing each other, right one above left. See a golden ball of light between the hands. Expand the light with each breath for 10-15 minutes.

The Navel Center & Elimination

1. On back, bicycle alternate legs 1-1½ feet above the ground with long deep breathing, 1-2 minutes.
2. Inhale while raising straight legs to 90 degrees, and exhale, lowering them. Continue rapidly for 1 minute. Rest for 30 seconds. Repeat twice.
3. On stomach, rise up into Cobra Pose and try to kick buttocks with alternate legs, exhaling as you kick one leg, inhaling as you kick the other.
4. In Bow Pose on stomach, rock back and forth with the breath for 2 minutes.
5. On the back, clasp knees to chest and roll back and forth on the spine for 2 minutes.
6. In Baby Pose, sitting on heels, grasp heels and bend forward in Gurpranam with navel breathing for 1-2 minutes.
7. In Stretch Pose, raise heels and head 6 inches off the ground, keeping arms and legs straight, hands pointing to feet, eyes fixed on toes, and hold with Breath of Fire for 1-2 minutes.
8. On stomach, hands in Venus Lock and stretched overhead, arms hugging ears, raise arms, head, chest, and (straight) legs and hold with Breath of Fire for 1-2 minutes.
9. While standing with arms at sides, sway like a pendulum, inhaling as you bend left, exhaling as you bend right, for 2 minutes.

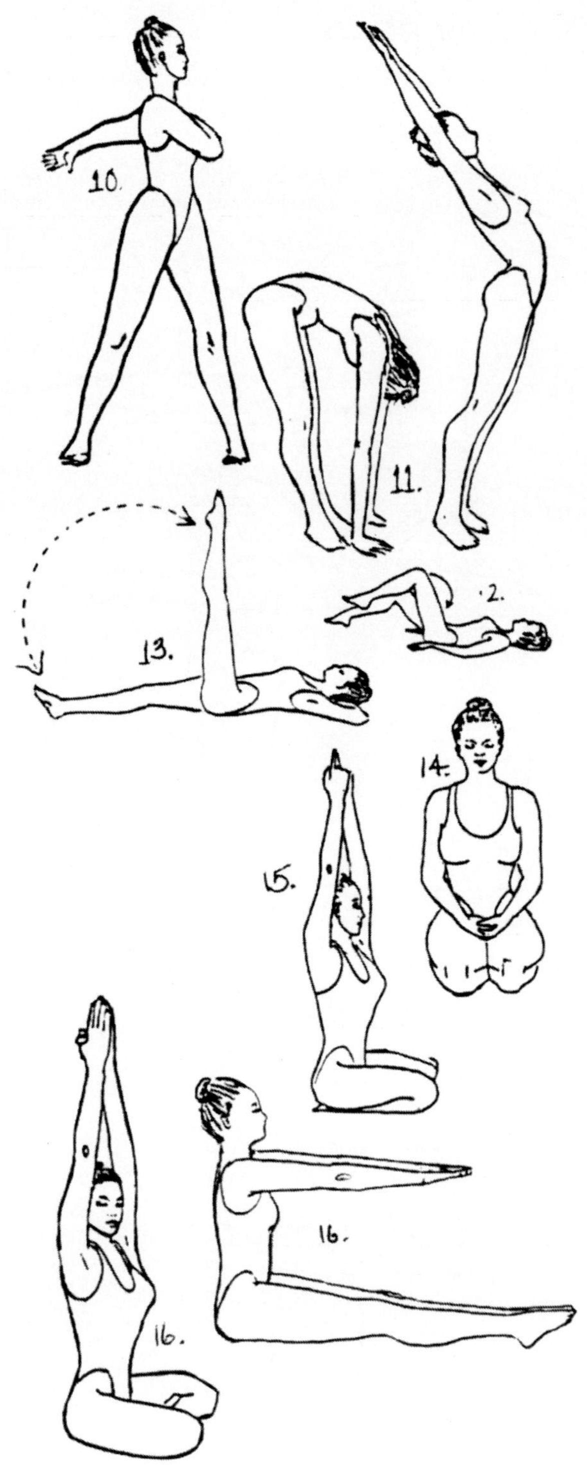

10. Still standing, inhale and twist the body to the left, extending the left arm, right hand goes to the heart. Then exhale as you twist right, right hand extended, left hand to the heart. Continue briskly for 2 minutes.

11. Standing, exhale and touch palms, if possible, flat on the ground in front of feet, thumbs crossed. Then inhaling, straighten up and arch backwards, holding the breath in for 10-20 seconds. Repeat 10-20 times.

12. Repeat bicycle exercise (#1) for 1-2 minutes.

13. On back with hands in Venus Lock behind the neck, raise alternate legs to 90 degrees at a fast pace for 2 minutes.

14. In Rock Pose, hands in Venus Lock on the lap, mentally inhale "Sat," exhale "Nam," with a soft, rhythmic breath for 1-2 minutes.

15. Perform Sat Kriya (see page 103) for 2 minutes. (Hands in Venus Lock, index fingers extended, or palms together overhead, repeat "Sat" pulling in navel, and "Nam" relaxing it.)

16. Stretch arms and legs straight out in front with Breath of Fire for 2 minutes.

17. In Easy Pose, hands raised overhead, arms hugging ears, palms together, look to third eye and chant for 3-5 minutes:

    EK ONG KAAR
    SAT NAM
    SIRI WAH-HAY GURU

    Then relax deeply on your back.

Kundalini Kriya #7

1. On back, raise arms to 60 degrees, inhale, and hold the breath for 1 minute. Exhale, inhale, raise legs to 60 degrees, hold for 3 seconds, and exhale down. Inhale, raise both legs to 60 degrees, and hold for 1 minute. Then press toes forward, heels together, exhale, inhale, and hold for 15 seconds. Relax.

2. On back, raise one shoulder off the ground and bring it back to the ground without using the rest of the body, and then repeat on the other side. Do this exercise very slowly so you can be aware of and release tension in the shoulders and upper back. Repeat for 1-2 minutes.

3. While sitting, bring one knee to the chest, raise the other outstretched leg 12 inches off the ground, and swing it out to the side in an arc from the hip for 1 minute. Switch legs and repeat. Repeat the exercise on the first leg, and then a second time on the second leg.

   3b. In Rock Pose, sitting on heels, do Spinal Flexes (see Warm Up Exercises) rapidly for 1-2 minutes.

   3c. Continue Spinal Flexes with arms stretched out in front for 1-2 minutes.

4. Still in Rock Pose, lean back, support your weight on your elbows and forearms, and do neck rolls for 1-2 minutes. This is good for the thyroid.

5. On back, rapidly raise and lower alternate shoulders as in #2. Inhale up, exhale down. Great exercise for the heart.

6. a. On stomach, raise head and legs only, leaving arms on the ground stretched out over the head, hands in Venus Lock. Hold with Breath of Fire for 1 minute.

   b. Extend arms straight out behind back, hands clasped in Venus Lock, raise upper body, stick out curled tongue, and do Breath of Fire for 1 minute.

7. Come up into Cobra Pose, supporting the body with the arms, and say HUM. Relax down and say HUM. Feel the vibration of HUM at your heart and in your spine. Continue for 1-2 minutes.

8. Relax on your stomach and then turn over and relax on your back.

One thing you cannot escape is challenge. Whether you challenge the challenge or you give in to the challenge, that is what decides your spirituality. Is your spirit higher than the challenge so you can face it? It is simple. If your face and your grace does not give in to the challenge, you are spiritual. Otherwise you are not. Period.

Fish Fry Kriya

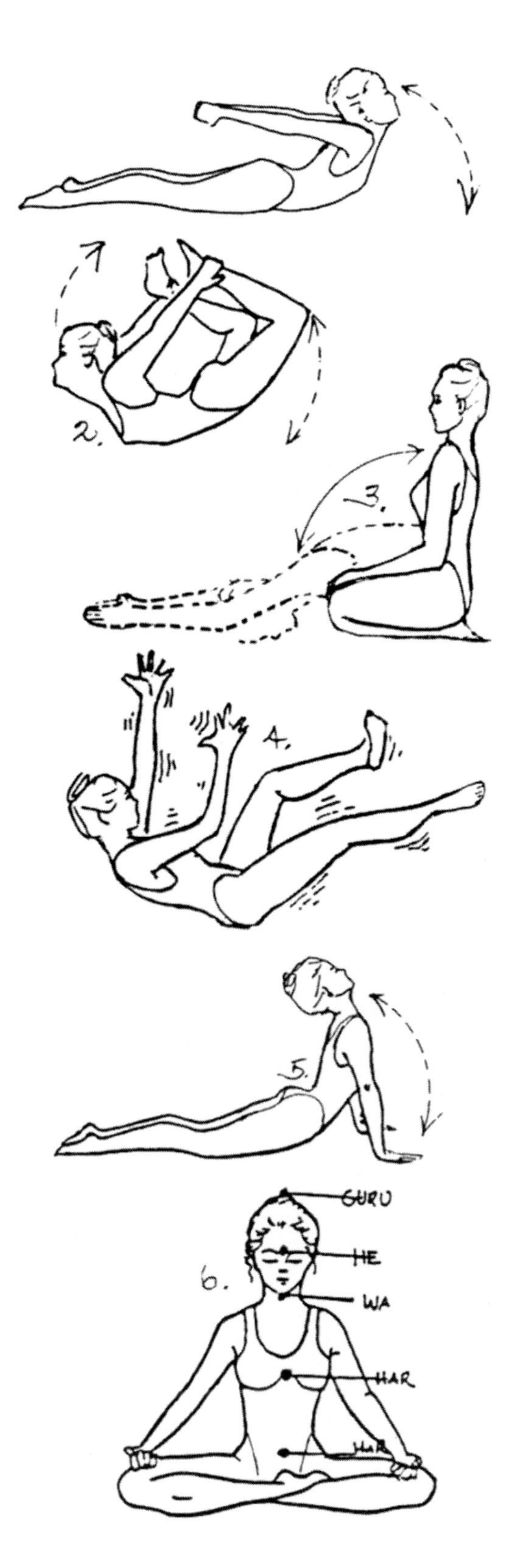

1. On stomach, clasp hands in Venus Lock behind back and inhale as you raise torso as high as possible into modified Cobra Pose. Exhale down and back up 26 times. Be sure to use the root lock while you come up. You can relax the root lock as you come down. (Opens the heart and energizes the thoracic region.) Relax on the stomach.

2. Rocking Bow Pose: Allowing the breath to move you, rock back and forth in Bow Pose 26 times with arms reaching back and holding on to ankles. (Produces energy to revitalize the cells and keep you young.)

3. Rock Pose into forward bowing: Sitting on heels, inhale in sitting position; exhale bending forward to touch forehead to ground, extending arms out in front in Prayer Pose, 26 times. (For focus and elimination.)

4. Lying on back, imagine being a living fish thrown into a red-hot skillet, and move and flop about for 3 minutes. (Only when you *act* like someone with no control over your nervous system, can you have control.) Relax on your back.

5. Lying on stomach, place hands under shoulders and push up into Cobra Pose, slowly inhaling up and exhaling down. Keep elbows bent to focus on bending the upper spine. Maintain root lock as you come up, and release it as you come down. Avoid overextension of the lower spine. Do 26 Cobra Pushups. Relax on your stomach.

6. Meditate as you internally chant for 11 minutes:

    HAR at the navel point
    HAR at the heart center
    WA at the throat center
    HE at the third eye
    GURU at the crown center

    Relax, meditate.

For Drug Damage

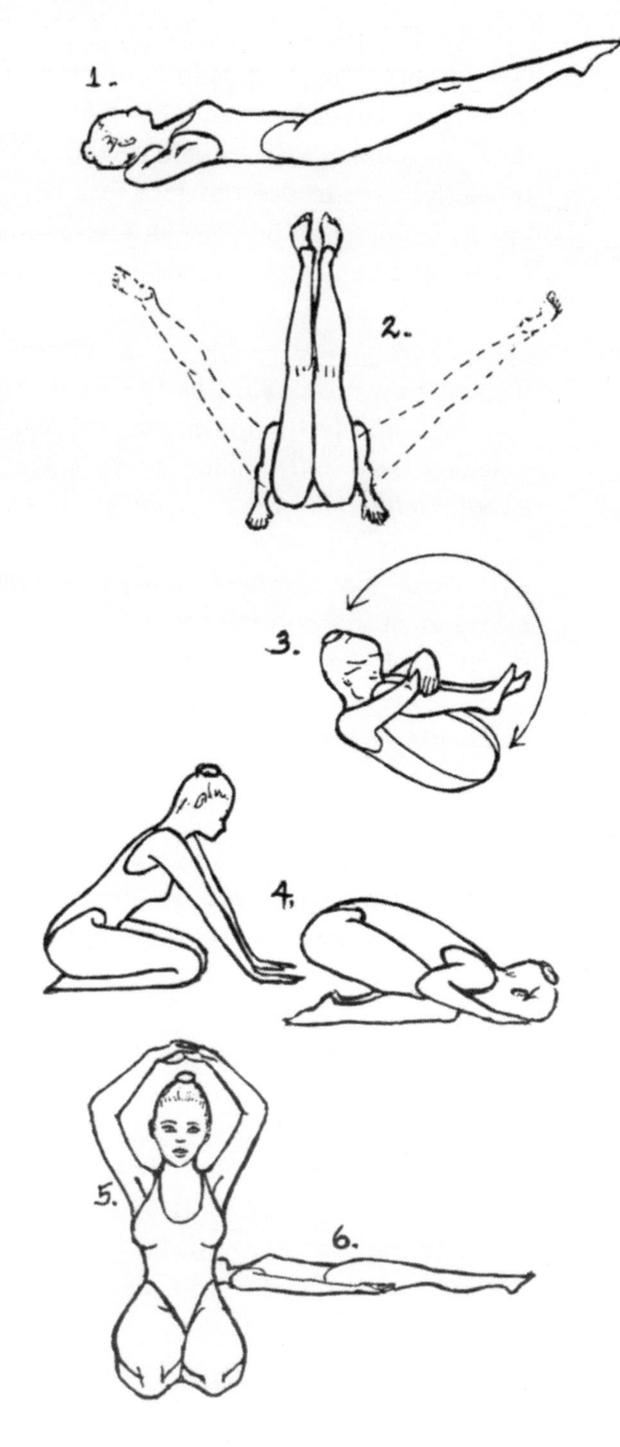

1. On back with hands in Venus Lock behind the neck, raise straight legs to 24 inches and hold with long deep breathing for 1-3 minutes.

2. Still on back, raise legs to 90 degrees, inhale and spread them wide; exhale and bring them together. Repeat and continue for 1-3 minutes.

3. Bring knees to chest, wrap arms around legs, and roll back and forth on the spine for 1-3 minutes.

4. In Rock Pose, sitting on heels, place hands 8 inches in front of the knees. Inhale, then exhale as you bend forward, placing forehead on the floor. Inhale up and exhale down for 1-3 minutes.

5. Still in Rock Pose, place hands in Venus Lock above the head and chant for 3-11 minutes:

   HUM, HUM, HUM

   ("Hum" means "We the total Universe.")
   Create a vibration in the center of your head.

6. Relax in Corpse Pose on the back.

COMMENTS: This kriya strengthens the navel center and nervous system and opens the third eye and crown chakras gradually and naturally. The meditation with the mantra HUM opens your crown chakra and soothes your whole being with the cosmic sound.

You can experience many benefits from practicing this short set and Sat Kriya for 40, 90, or 120 days. Whatever your current condition, Kundalini Yoga heals your system at a pace and in the progression suited to where you are at.

Serabandanda Kriya

Keep Your Body Healthy

As a warm up, you may wish to stand up and shake every part of your body to let go of stress and release your vital energy.

1. Begin in Triangle Pose, heels on floor, hands and feet one foot apart from each other. Hands and feet remain in place throughout.

2. From Triangle Pose, inhale, exhale, and lower chin only in a push up movement to the floor. You can bend your knees, placing your knees on the floor. Modify to suit your arm strength.

3. Inhale and exhale into Cobra Pose, back arched, arms and legs straight.

4. Inhale back into Triangle Pose on toes; then exhale and lower heels.

Repeat the above sequence, gradually working up to 26 times and then relax 5-10 minutes. More advanced students can repeat the exercise (gradually working up to 26 times), followed by the relaxation period, one or two more times.

COMMENTS: This kriya creates the environment for the body to heal. It opens valves in the veins and arteries for complete circulation. It opens the vertebrae to allow blood to flow through every part of the spine and then to every part of the body.

Gurpranam

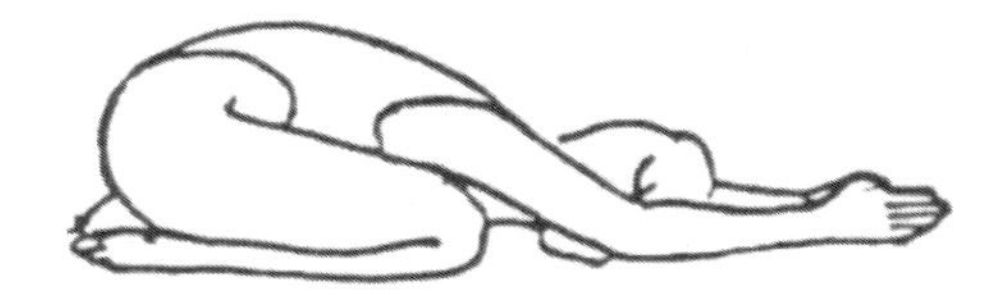

Gurpranam is a restful posture that can be done after any kriya or meditation. Sit on heels in Rock Pose, bending down to rest forehead on the floor in front of the knees. Stretch the arms straight out overhead, palms together, and rest there with long deep breathing for 2 or more minutes. Let go, surrender, and trust!

> Yogi Bhajan wants us all to be great. I remember Yogi Bhajan telling us, "Excuses are excuses."
>
> 

Raise Kundalini in Quick Order

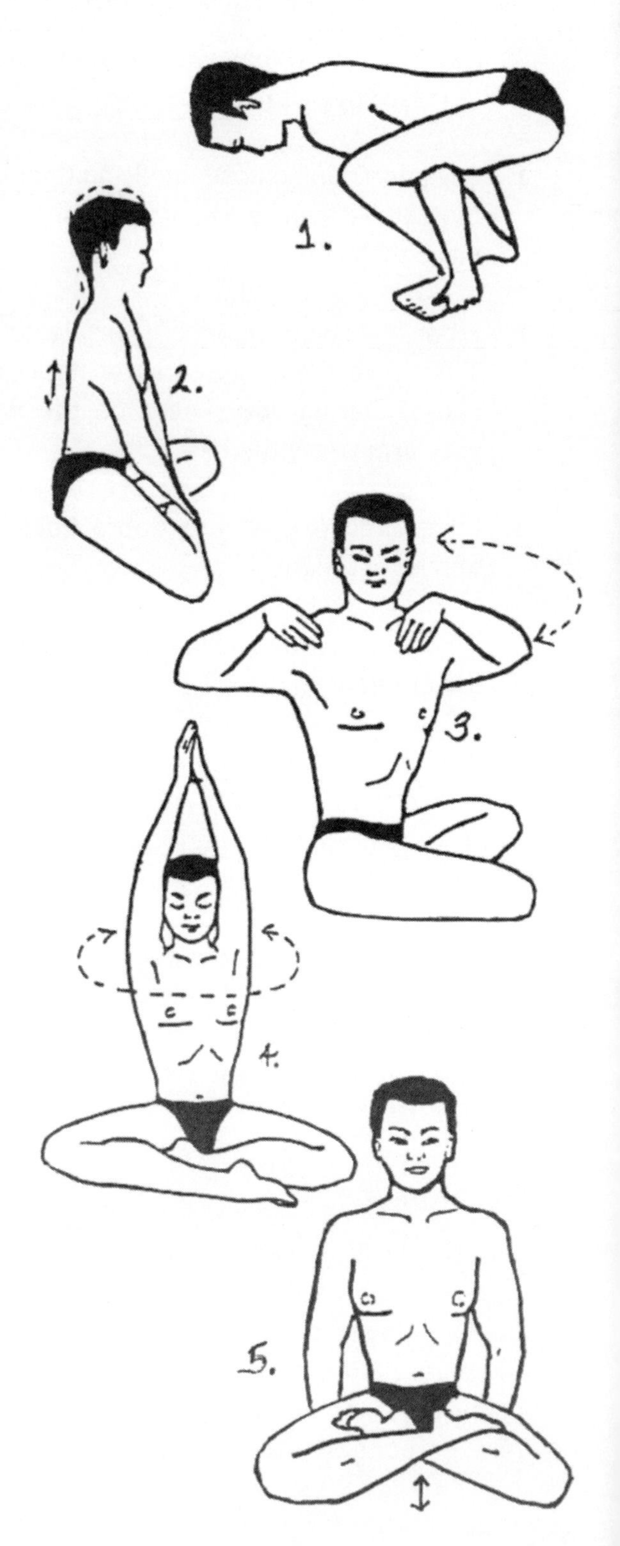

1. Chair Pose: Squat down with feet 1½-2 feet apart. Pass arms inside thighs and outside calves, placing hands under heels, thighs resting on the elbows, spine parallel to the floor. Hold with long deep breathing for 2-5 minutes. Then inhale, exhale, and apply Mulbhand. Balances the sex glands.

2. In Easy Pose, holding on to the shins, stretch and contract the spine up and down from the base for 2-3 minutes. (Without backwards and forward movements, there may be pain near the kidneys.) Inhale, exhale, and apply Mulbhand.

3. Spinal Twists with hands on shoulders, fingers forward, thumbs back. Inhale left, exhale right. Feel it at the navel point. Continue for 2-3 minutes.

4. Spinal Twists with arms straight up, palms together overhead, for 2-3 minutes. Then inhale, exhale, and pull Mulbhand. For ninth vertebra.

5. Body Drops in Lotus Pose, if possible, or with legs stretched out in front. Weight is on the fists beside the hips. Lift the buttocks and drop them down again for 2 minutes. (Do not perform Body Drops if pregnant, during your moon cycle, or if you experience pain while doing the movement.)

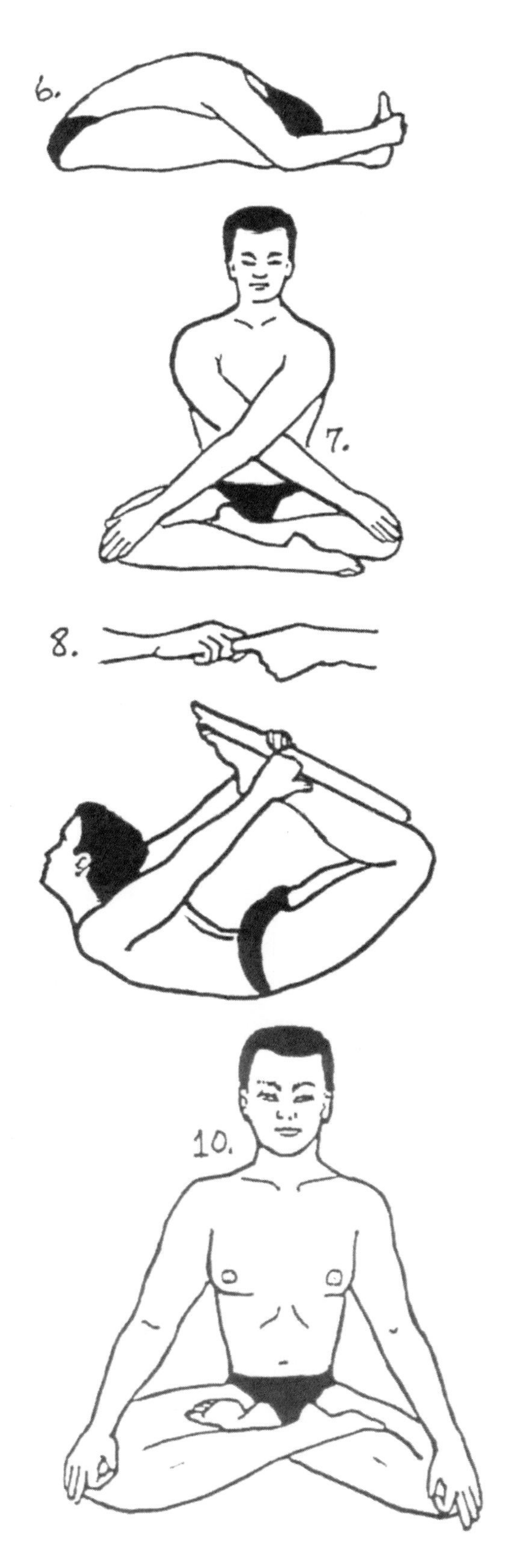

6. With legs stretched straight out in front, stretch body forward and relax down, head on knees, for 2-3 minutes. Then inhale, exhale, and pull Mulbhand.

7. In Easy Pose, cross arms, placing hands on opposite knees. Inhale deeply, pulling the arms and stretching the shoulders, and holding the breath in. Exhale and relax. Repeat the sequence for 2-3 minutes.

8. Lock index fingers at the heart center and pull hard with long deep breathing for 2-3 minutes. Then inhale, stretch arms above the head, and hold. Exhale, hold, and apply Mahabhand.

9. Bow Pose: On stomach, grab ankles and arch up, pulling arms and legs as high as possible. Inhale, stretch up even higher, hold, and pull Mulbhand. Release the lock. Then repeat inhale, stretch up, and pulling Mulbhand for 1-3 minutes.

10. Meditation: Fix eyes on top of the skull and press the tongue to the roof of the mouth. (There may be pain in the nose.) Enjoy the natural flow of your breath. Dedicate self to the Divine.

COMMENTS: This is an excellent preparation for deep meditation.

Advanced Kundalini Set #3

This is a more advanced set, but can be done by beginners using the minimum times. Be sure to apply the root lock at the end of each exercise. Done with the locks, powerful effects can be created with minimum times.

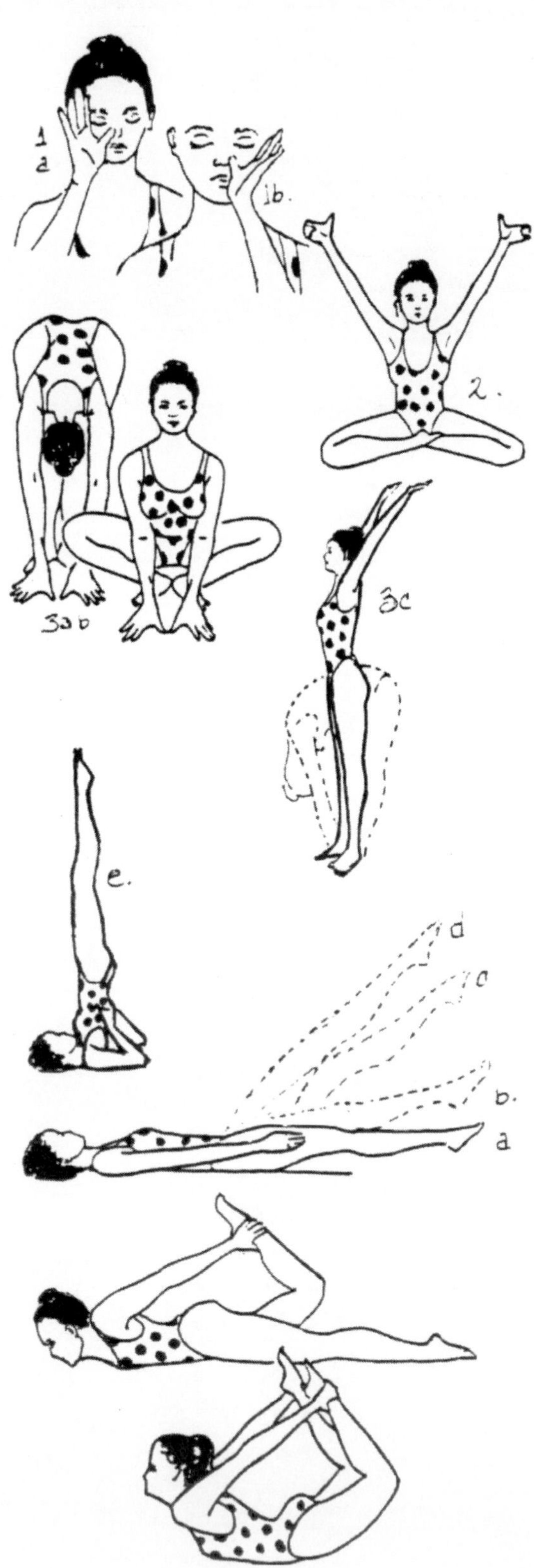

1. Left nostril breathing for 2-3 minutes. Then right nostril breathing for 2-3 minutes.

2. Ego Eradicator: In Easy Pose, extend arms up to 60 degrees, curl fingers in toward pads, thumbs pointing up, and do Breath of Fire for 2-3 minutes.

3. a) Do Frog Pose 10-26 times, inhaling up and exhaling down.
   b) Do Frog Pose 10-26 times again, this time exhaling up, inhaling down.
   c) Inhale, stand up, and stretch arms overhead, arching the back; then exhale and bend forward to touch the floor 10-26 times.

4. On back, keeping both legs straight, hands can be under the hips to protect the small of the back, do Breath of Fire in each of the given positions for 30 seconds to 2 minutes. Beginners start with minimum times. Be sure to relax between positions and feel the pulse at your navel.
   a) Raise legs 6 inches.
   b) Raise legs 12 inches.
   c) Raise legs up to 45 degrees.
   d) Raise legs to 60 degrees and hold.
   e) Lift torso into Shoulder Stand and hold.

5. a) One-Half Bow Pose with chin on ground and left hand holding right ankle with Breath of Fire for 1-2 minutes.
   b) As above but reversed, with right hand holding left ankle, for 1-2 minutes.
   c) Bow Pose with both hands holding corresponding ankles for 1-2 minutes.

6. a) Life-Nerve Stretch with both legs stretched out in front; inhale up and exhale down for 1-2 minutes.
   b) Life-Nerve Stretch in same position with Breath of Fire for 1-2 minutes. To end, inhale, exhale, and pull Mulbhand and hold.

7. a) Celibate Pose: (or on your knees or legs stretched out if needed) Lie on back with hips on floor between ankles and do Breath of Fire for 1-2 minutes.
   b) Upright Celibate Pose: While kneeling, sit between shins and feet with long deep breathing for 2-8 minutes.
   c) Camel Pose with Breath of Fire for 1-2 minutes.

8. Sat Kriya in Siddhasana (a.k.a. Perfect or Accomplished Pose): Sit with left heel in perineum (between anus and sex organ) and place right heel on top of left calf, tucking toes in between thigh and calf crease. Raise both arms overhead, palms together (or in Venus Lock with index fingers extending up) and chant

SAT

Pulling on the navel, then chant

NAM

Relaxing contraction. (See Sat Kriya, page 103.)
Continue for 3-5 minutes.

9. On back, raise legs to 6 inches (hands can be under hips) and hold with Breath of Fire for 30 seconds to 2 minutes. Then deeply relax on the back.

Spinal Awakening and Centering

The time for each exercise depends on how much time you have available, how long it takes to feel the stimulation, and the ability of your body to do the exercise.

1. Spinal Flexes: In Easy Pose, grasping ankles, inhale, arching the back forward at the waist, and exhale, contracting it back. On the forward movement, pull up slightly on the back of the neck to lengthen the spine. The head does not bob up and down. For first and second chakras.

2. Spinal Flexes: Then place hands on knees with elbows straight and continue arching and contracting the spine with the breath. Move from the upper spine.

3. Spinal Flexes: Then in Rock Pose, seated on heels, hands on knees, continue with Spinal Flexes, moving at the heart center.

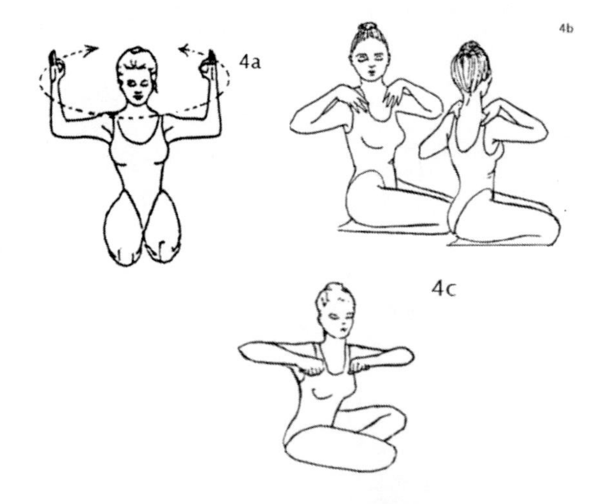

4. Spinal Twists: Sitting on heels, (a) with upper arms parallel to the ground and out to the sides, forearms up at 90 degrees, hands in Gyan Mudra (thumb and index fingers joined), inhale, twist left; exhale, twist right. (b) Still sitting on heels, hands on shoulders, fingers in front, thumbs in back, inhale, twist to the left; exhale to the right. Opens heart chakra. (c) Still on heels, hands in fists, thumb inside, at armpit level, inhale, twist left, exhale right.

5. Shoulder Shrugs: Shrug shoulders up reaching toward the ears on the inhale; exhale, relax down. Moves energy from heart to throat, releases shoulder tension, and stimulates heart, thymus, and throat center.

5

6. Neck stretches and rolls: Still on knees or in Easy Pose, first, slowly bend the head from side to side. Then roll the head gently in small circles, ironing out kinks as you go. Then reverse directions and continue. Keep the spine straight. Pull up on the neck and feel the head floating on the spine. For thyroid and releasing tension in the neck.

7. Eye exercises with the eyes closed. Any sequence is fine, but here is a complete sequence:
    - Look up, down, to the right, to the left, 10 o'clock to 4 o'clock, 11 to 5, 1 to 7, 2 to 8.
    - Make counterclockwise circles and then clockwise.
    - Make figure 8s up and down, right to left, 10 o'clock to 4 o'clock, 11 to 5, 1 to 7, 2 to 8.
    - Switch directions of figure 8s.

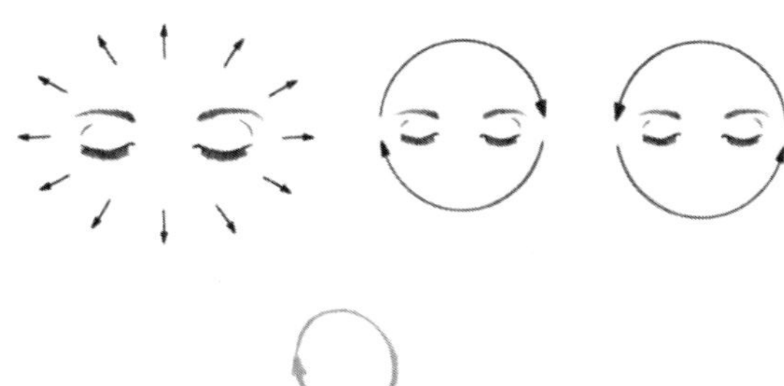

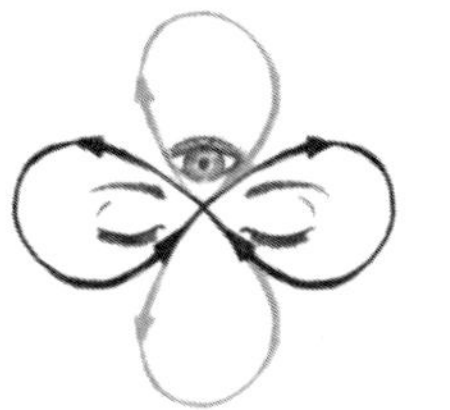

8. Repeat neck rolls. Notice the difference.

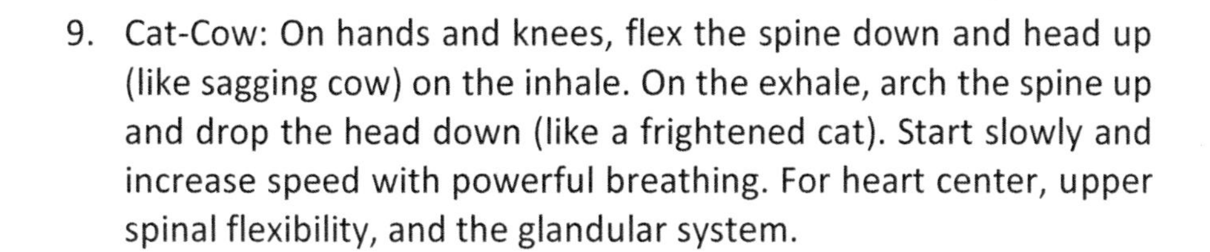

9. Cat-Cow: On hands and knees, flex the spine down and head up (like sagging cow) on the inhale. On the exhale, arch the spine up and drop the head down (like a frightened cat). Start slowly and increase speed with powerful breathing. For heart center, upper spinal flexibility, and the glandular system.

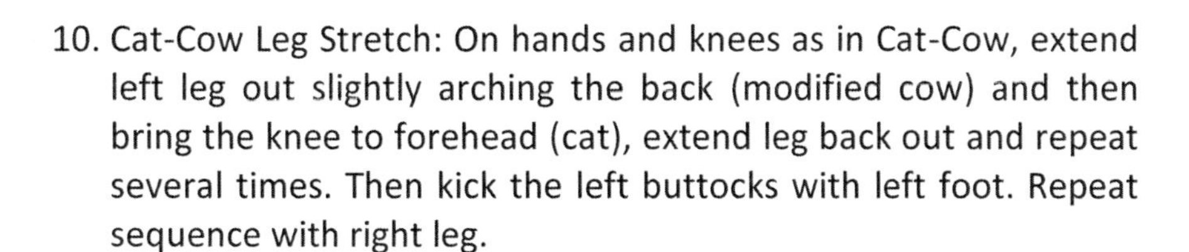

10. Cat-Cow Leg Stretch: On hands and knees as in Cat-Cow, extend left leg out slightly arching the back (modified cow) and then bring the knee to forehead (cat), extend leg back out and repeat several times. Then kick the left buttocks with left foot. Repeat sequence with right leg.

11. Breath of Fire in Cow Pose, activating the chakras from the crown down to the base. Spend at least 5 seconds on each chakra.

12. Breath of Fire in Cat Pose starting at the base of the spine and working up the chakras.

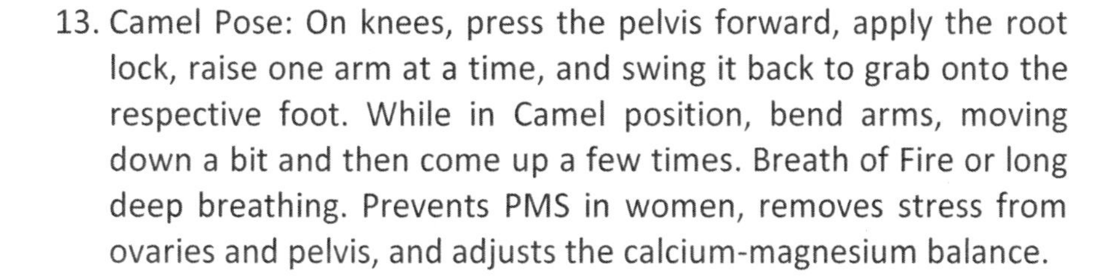

13. Camel Pose: On knees, press the pelvis forward, apply the root lock, raise one arm at a time, and swing it back to grab onto the respective foot. While in Camel position, bend arms, moving down a bit and then come up a few times. Breath of Fire or long deep breathing. Prevents PMS in women, removes stress from ovaries and pelvis, and adjusts the calcium-magnesium balance.

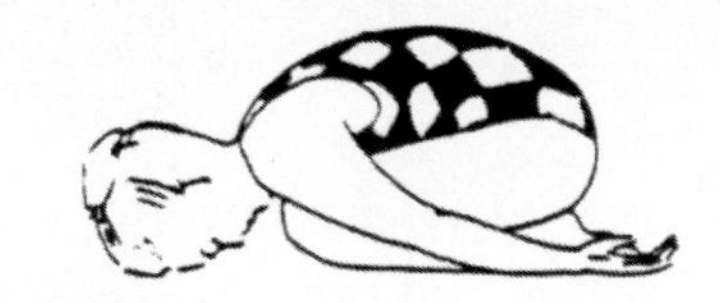

14. Rest in Baby Pose, breathe into kidneys, focus at third eye.

15. Sat Kriya: Sit on heels, arms are straight overhead with elbows hugging ears, fingers interlocked with index fingers extended straight up. Pull in on the navel with SAT and allow a light root lock. As you chant NAM, relax the navel and the lock. Feel the wave up and down the spine. After 3-5 minutes, inhale and delicately squeeze the energy up with the root lock from the base of the spine to the top of the skull and out the hands. Exhale and repeat 2 more times. Relax down. Focus inside your skin to consolidate and contain your energy. Follow with a deep relax to integrate.

16. Deep Relaxation: After exercising, relax completely on your back, enjoying aliveness, flow, and an expansive space.

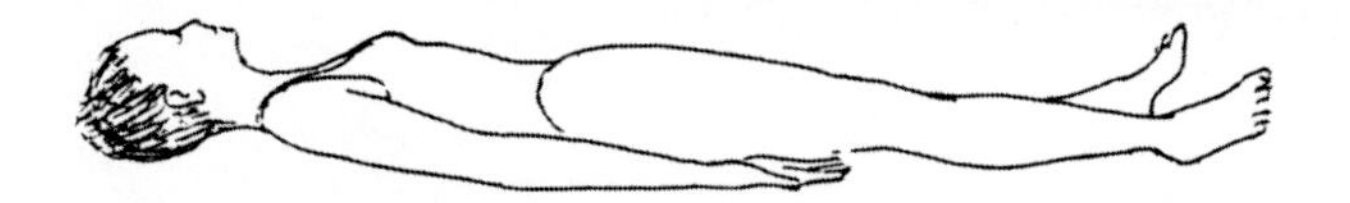

Rock and Roll on the spine from the base to the neck, knees clasped to chest, nose between knees. Inhale forward, exhale back. Circulates energy in the entire spine.

17. Meditation: Sitting in meditation pose, chant any divine mantra for 3-11 minutes.

Monitor your mood before and after doing this set and enjoy the results.

> In small things lies all things. Spell the word small: S-M-A-L-L. Take away the SM, it is ALL. In every small effort, there is all the effort. If you put all the effort into every small effort, you'll be a saint. You don't need a degree. Why should we be a saint? I am asking a question. It's the most selfish enactment and desire. Why? Once you become a saint, the totality works for you. Reality serves you. Infinity is around you. If you are not, you sweat, you hassle.

Happy Hips

The time for each exercise depends on how much time you have available, how long it takes to feel the stimulation, and the ability of your body to do the exercise. Do the first three exercises with Breath of Fire or long deep breathing.

1. Life-Nerve Stretch: (a) With left heel pulled into groin, stretch out over outstretched right leg and hold with powerful Breath of Fire. Grab onto your big toe or where possible on your leg, but keep the leg straight. Flex the heel forward and press the toes back toward the head to stretch the hamstrings up through the sciatic nerve. Keep the spine straight. Do not bend at the heart or bend your head toward your knee. Relieves tension in the small of the back, moves energy up the spine, and prepares legs for sitting.

   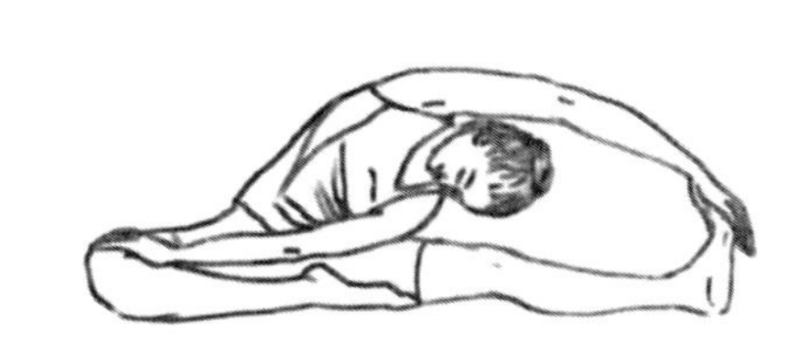

   (b) With the right leg, grab onto the left knee with the right hand. Bring the left arm over your head as you stretch toward the right leg. Then switch legs and repeat (a) and (b) on the other side.

2. Alternate Leg Stretches with legs wide apart:
   (a) Inhale up at center and exhale as you stretch the heart toward alternate knees. Grab onto your big toe or where possible on your leg, but keep the leg straight, stretching from the hips. Keep spine straight. Do not bend at the heart or bend your head toward your knee. Opens the pelvis.

   (b) With legs wide apart, stretch to right side with left arm over the head and right arm reaching toward or holding on to the right foot. Do both (a) and (b) on the opposite side.

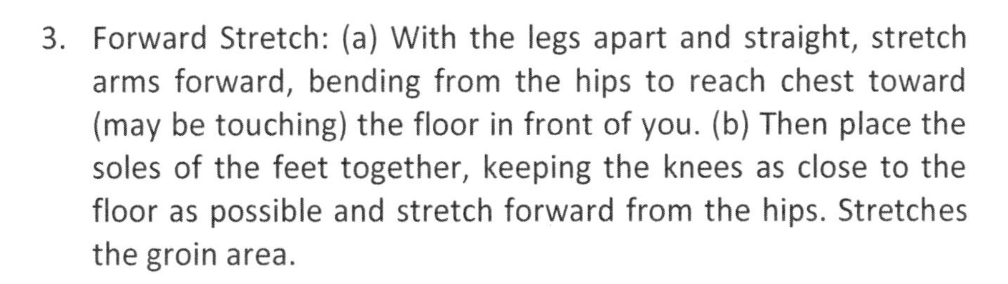

3. Forward Stretch: (a) With the legs apart and straight, stretch arms forward, bending from the hips to reach chest toward (may be touching) the floor in front of you. (b) Then place the soles of the feet together, keeping the knees as close to the floor as possible and stretch forward from the hips. Stretches the groin area.

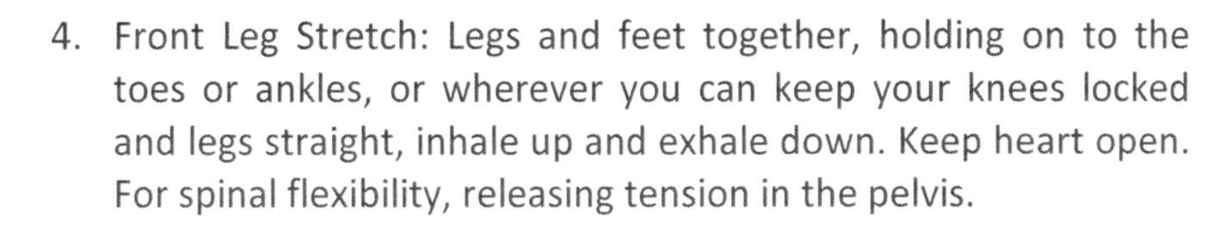

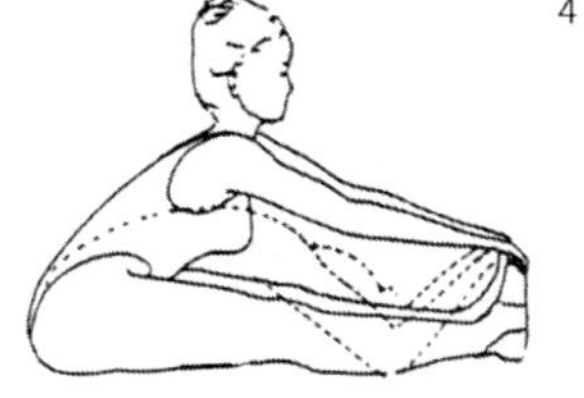

4. Front Leg Stretch: Legs and feet together, holding on to the toes or ankles, or wherever you can keep your knees locked and legs straight, inhale up and exhale down. Keep heart open. For spinal flexibility, releasing tension in the pelvis.

5. Groin Stretch: Sit with soles of feet together, heels touching groin, hands grasping feet. Slowly move the knees up and down toward the floor, stretching the inner thigh muscles. Then slowly bend forward, stretching the hips to bring the heart toward the floor. Releases tension in the groin, adjusts hips, facilitates sitting in meditation.

6. Spinal Twists: Seated in Easy Pose, cross the left leg over the right knee. Right arm reaches around the outside of the left leg and grabs the left foot or ankle, twisting the spine and neck to look over the left shoulder. Sit evenly on both buttocks, not on the heel, and keep the spine perfectly straight. Hold the pose with Breath of Fire for 6 minutes. Inhale, hold, pull root lock and relax. Reverse arms and legs and repeat. Then relax with long deep breathing for 2-3 minutes. (The longer you remain in the pose, the easier it is to maintain.)

7. Leg lifts on back: Raise legs, alternately or together to 90 degrees. Inhale up, exhale down, 5-20 times. Keep small of the back on the ground by engaging your abdominal muscles and applying the root lock. Strengthens abdominal muscles, builds core, and sets navel.

8. Plow Pose: Lying on back, raise both legs to 90 degrees, and then bring them over the head into Plow Pose, stretching the spine, toes touching the floor, if possible, above the head. To end, bend the knees and stretch further. Hold for up to 1 minute.

9. Shoulder Stand: Using the arms for support, elbows on floor, position the rest of the body so it is perpendicular to the floor from shoulders to toes; weight on shoulders, elbows, and neck, with chin pressed into chest. Kick the buttocks for part of the 1-3 minutes.

10. Alternate leg kicks: On back with legs wide apart, feet raised about 2 feet off the floor, legs straight, alternately extend each leg with the inhale, and on the exhale, bring the heel as close to the groin as possible, maintaining the 2 foot elevation, for 1-2 minutes. Relax.

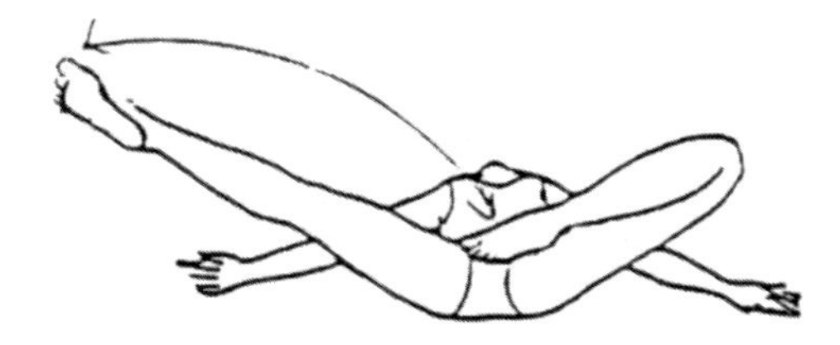

11. Push Pulls: Lift both legs 1-2 feet and begin a push-pull motion, alternating between bending one knee toward the chest, moving from hips, and lowering the leg so it is parallel to the ground but still elevated, for 1-2 minutes. Rest 2 minutes and repeat cycle if you wish.

12. Sit Ups: Sit with knees bent, feet on the floor, arms folded in front of the chest. Lean back as far as you can, maintaining root lock and keeping the spine straight. Inhale as you lean back and exhale as you come up: (a) First lean straight back and come up, (b) then lean back, twisting to the left; come up, and then (c) back to the right and come up. For strengthening the abdominal muscles, core, and setting the navel point.

13. Lying on back, bend knees and clasp them to chest with the arms, allowing the head to relax back. Rest in this position for 1-3 minutes.

14. Centerline Stretch: From the above position, inhale, open the arms straight out to the sides to the ground, as you extend the legs straight out to 60 degrees. Exhale and return to original position. Repeat and continue for 1-5 minutes or 26 times. You can also do the same leg movements while moving your arms above your head.

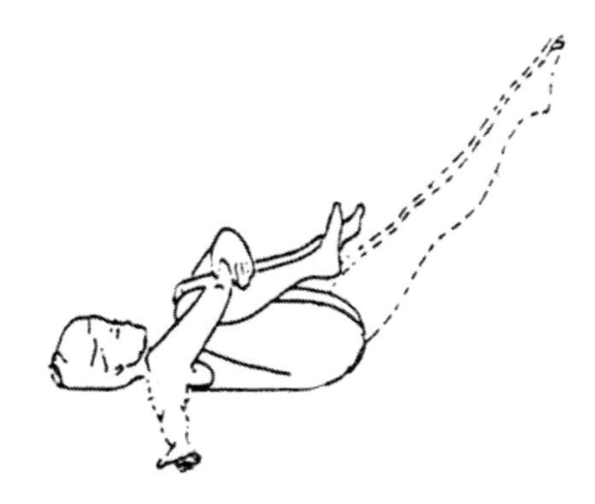

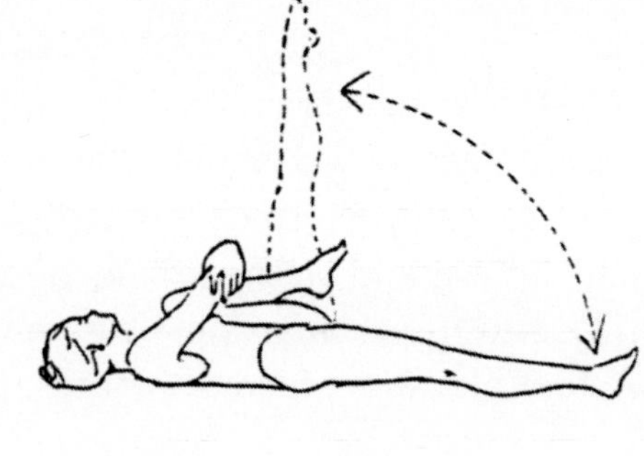

15. Alternate Leg Lifts: On back, bring one knee to the chest, hold it there with both hands, and rapidly raise and lower the other leg to 90 degrees, inhaling up, exhaling down for 1 minute or 26 times. Switch legs and repeat for 1 minute or 26 times. Repeat the complete cycle once more.

16. Cross-crawls: Alternately raise opposite arm and leg (right leg, left arm, then left leg, right arm) for 1-3 minutes.

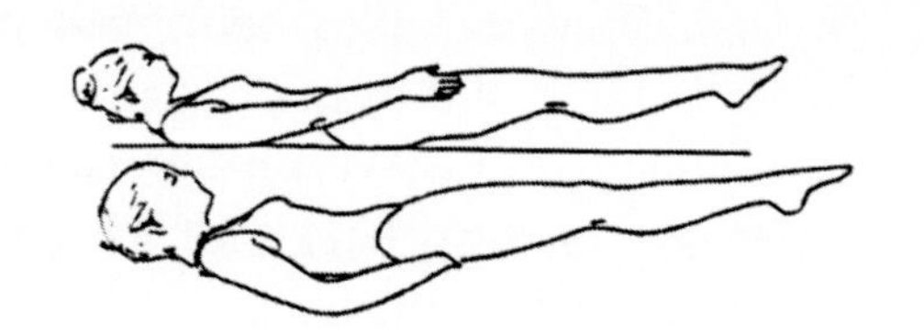

17. Stretch Pose: Lying on back, raise head and feet 6 inches off the ground and hold with Breath of Fire for 30 seconds to 2 minutes, or as long as possible. Eyes look at big toes. Hands face inward and point toward feet. If the small of the back comes up, place hands beneath hips for support. If held less than a minute, rest and repeat pose, increasing time as core muscles strengthen. Before coming down, apply root lock and set your navel. It's okay to start out by doing one leg at a time.

18. Deep Relaxation: After exercising, relax completely on your back, enjoying aliveness, flow, and an expansive space.

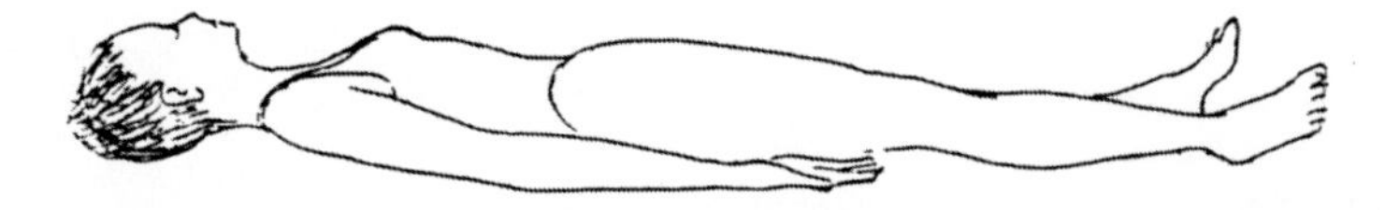

Rock and Roll on the spine from the base to the neck, knees clasped to chest, nose between knees. Inhale forward, exhale back. Circulates energy in the entire spine.

19. Meditation: Sitting in meditation pose, chant any divine mantra for 3-11 minutes.

Meditations

Long Sat Nams to Neutralize Tension

The simplest and most basic meditation in Kundalini Yoga is chanting long SAT NAMs.
SAT NAM is a *bij* or seed mantra. From the seed of SAT NAM the truth grows within us.

Sit with a straight spine in a cross-legged Easy Pose, in your preferred meditation posture, or in a chair with the feet on the floor, sit bones carrying the weight of the body.

Bring the hands to the heart, palms facing the chest, left hand on top of right. Place the left thumb in the center of the right palm. The fingers of both hands are together and straight. The hands gently rest against the chest; arms are relaxed against the body. Eyes are nine-tenths closed to start. As the meditation progresses, they may close completely. Inhale with a long deep breath. On the exhale chant out loud

SAAAAAAAAAAAAAAAAAAAAAAAAAAAAAAAT

At the end of the breath say **NAM**. NAM is short. The A is not drawn out as in the SAAAAAAAAT.

Then inhale deeply again and continue for 3 to 5 minutes, building to 11, 15, 22, or 31 minutes. Notice that your breath gets longer and deeper and may slow down to four or fewer breaths per minute. At the end of the meditation, inhale deeply, suspend the breath, listen inside, and be one with the experience. Do this three times. Then sit quietly or lie down and completely relax.

SAT is the liberator and the cleanser. Let yourself relax and release with the AAAAAAA.
NAM is like the anchor. Feel the sound anchor you in your body.

Feel the sound of the AAAAAA come from the heart. Experience your throat as the mouthpiece of your heart. This practice will help you locate, consolidate, and open up the fourth (heart) and the fifth (throat) chakras. SAT NAM is the call of the soul. As you chant, call out to your soul, sing to your soul. Singing to your soul creates a very peaceful feeling. It takes us out of duality for a moment as our personality and soul merge as one in the sound current of our infinite being. Feel free to express any emotions that arise with the sounds. This is a good way to release and balance the emotions. The emotional energy will be gently elevated into soul energy.

COMMENTS: This is a very relaxing meditation. It completely neutralizes tension and brings you to a very peaceful state. Do it for 40 days and you can revitalize your glandular system and reestablish your glandular equilibrium. This is a good meditation to do at the end of a busy day. Do it when you get home after work before dinner and you will be able to enjoy your evening. Do it before you go to bed and you will sleep like a baby.

Seven-Wave Sat Nam Meditation

Sit in Easy Pose, palms together in Prayer Mudra, with the eyes closed and focused at the brow point. Be aware of the centerline of your body in the center of your spine.

Inhale deeply and on the exhale chant the mantra SAAAAA AAAAA AAAAA ... in six waves up the spine from the first chakra (base of the spine) up to the sixth chakra (third eye). At each chakra chant a separate AAAAA. Feel the S at the base of the spine and then weave the AAAAA up the spine through each of the first six chakras. The "T" vibrates at the top of the head or crown chakra.

On NAM, let the energy and sound radiate from the seventh chakra at the top of the head through the aura. As the sound penetrates each chakra, gently pull, feel, or pay attention to the physical area it corresponds to. The locations of the chakras are as follows:

First — rectum
Second — sex organ
Third — navel
Fourth — heart
Fifth — throat
Sixth — between the eyebrows
Seventh — top of the head

Continue for 3-15 minutes.

COMMENTS: If you can, build this meditation a few seconds a day to 31 minutes (or more if you wish). The mind will be cleansed as the ocean waves wash the sandy beach. This is a bij (seed) mantra meditation. Bij mantras such as "Sat Nam" can totally rearrange the habit patterns of the subconscious mind. We all have habit patterns and couldn't function without them. But some patterns we have created are unwanted. To change, we have to eliminate these sabotaging thought patterns. By vibrating the sound current "Sat Nam" in this manner, you activate the energy of the mind to erase old habits and establish new ones. Consequently, this meditation is a good introduction to Kundalini Yoga. It will open the mind to new experiences. This meditation can be used to clear off the effects of a hurried day and before beginning another deep meditation. After chanting this mantra, you will feel calm, relaxed, and mellow. Sit quietly after chanting and enjoy the clear, quiet inner space.

Meditation for the Central Nervous System

Sit in Easy Pose with a straight spine. Relax the arms down to the sides of the body with the elbows bent, forearms up, hands near the shoulders, palms facing forward in Gyan Mudra (thumb and forefingers touching). Eyes are nine-tenths closed. Inhale, exhale, and with the breath held out, mentally vibrate

WHA — as you first pull the root lock

HAY — as you pull the diaphragm lock

GURU — as you apply the neck lock
(Pull up on the back of the neck and elongate the spine.)

The delicate application of the three locks will create a continuous wave-like motion in the spine. The whole spine will undulate.

Work up to repeating the complete three-part mantra a total of nine times on the held-out breath. Do not create tension to reach nine times. The body must be relaxed for the energy to circulate and move up the spine.

Continue the sequence for 5-11 minutes and slowly build time to a maximum of 31 minutes.

COMMENTS: This meditation activates the sushumna nadi (central channel in the spine) and strengthens the central nervous system. Done with awareness, it will bring about deep inner awakening in an individual who practices it.

We have the right to be happy and excellent. It all depends on how we meditate and direct our mind—ourselves, or let it be directed by circumstances. Many people have good things by good luck, but without a meditative mind, they lose consistency and act as a loose caboose.

Kirtan Kriya — Sa Ta Na Ma Meditation

Kirtan Kriya, often referred to as the SA TA NA MA meditation, is the most important meditation in Kundalini Yoga. It was one of the first meditations taught by Yogi Bhajan and remains today as a foundational meditation, recommended for every student of Kundalini Yoga. Yogi Bhajan said that if you can do only one meditation, this is it. It does everything for you in the order that you need. It is your teacher. And as you practice it, you will come to realize that it is your best friend. Whatever you need at the moment, it will readjust and align you to bring balance into your mind and thus your life.

This meditation is given for everything from breaking habits to achieving emotional balance. I knew one woman who had been very emotionally upset for over two weeks. Finally she went to a quiet spot in the woods and did 31 minutes of Kirtan Kriya and voila! she felt relaxed and whole again. It helps you focus and center yourself. It is a catalyst for change because it is a very powerful spiritual cleanser. You may go through a lot because you will be releasing a lot. Be present to what you are experiencing and be willing to let it all go. The process will allow you to give all your garbage back to God. If you want to maintain the status quo, don't do this meditation. If you are willing to change and welcome a new dimension of being into your life, this meditation is for you.

There is another great benefit of this meditation. Do you think about an old lover and want to be liberated from the grips of the past and release him or her from your aura? This is the meditation! There is nothing more powerful to release the auric pain people suffer when they break up with a lover. It will reestablish your aura as your own. Practice for 40 days (or more as needed) to complete this process.

The bottom line is that this meditation works. All you have to do is do it. You can trust the process and the technology. Over time, the mind awakens to the infinite quality of the soul. This meditation is so basic to Kundalini Yoga that it is recommended to practice it for 1,000 days.

Meditation Instructions

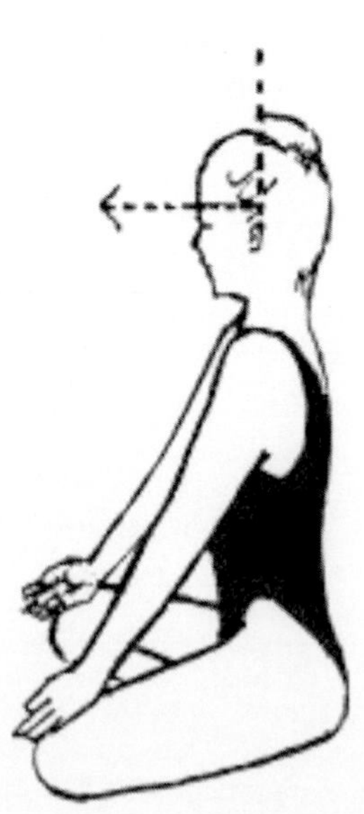

Sit with a straight spine and meditate at the brow point, chanting with the hands on the knees, elbows straight:

On SA, touch the Jupiter (index) finger to the thumb on each hand.
On TA, the Saturn (middle) fingers and thumbs touch.
On NA, the ring fingers and the thumbs touch.
On MA, the Mercury (little fingers) and thumbs touch.
The pressure is about 5-10 pounds and should not create stress.

Visualize or feel each sound making a 90-degree turn in the center of the head at the third eye, and project it out to infinity through the forehead.

31-Minute Version

For the first 5 minutes, chant *out loud* (the voice of humans).

For the second 5 minutes, chant in an *audible whisper* (the language of lovers).

For the next 10 minutes, chant *silently* (the language of the Divine). Continue the finger movements. Keep visualizing the mantra moving in an "L" from the top of the head and out the third eye. Use the mouth to make the sounds, even though they are silent.

Then for 5 minutes, *whisper*.

End with 5 minutes *out loud*.

During the last (31st) minute, listen inside and hear the mantra and experience the "L" in the head, not the finger movements.

11-Minute Version

Kirtan Kriya can also be done for shorter times. Yogi Bhajan said that during these stressful times it should be done for at least 11 minutes every day. For the 11-minute version do

2 minutes *out loud*

2 minutes in an *audible whisper*

3 minutes *silently*, keeping the fingers, "L" in the head, and tongue moving

2 minutes *whisper*

2 minutes *out loud*

Sit quietly, listen to the mantra chant back to you, and feel the vibration in your body.

> If you are willing to look at another person's behavior toward you as a reflection of the state of their relationship with themselves rather than a statement about your value as a person, then you will, over a period of time cease to react at all.

Brainwave Meditation

When our brainwaves are stable and we are in our neutral mind, we do not react to every little annoyance. And when we do not react, we are mentally available to respond appropriately to situations as they arise. This meditation specifically changes our brainwaves so that we feel more stable and neutral in our life situations.

Sit in Easy Pose with a straight spine. Bring arms comfortably to the sides of the body with the elbows bent. Hands in fists, with the thumbs over the last three fingers, facing forward. Hold the index finger straight up, tight and stable, but without tensing the rest of the arms and body. The forearms should be perpendicular to the ground. During the meditation, check the position and move the elbows forward as needed to maintain the position.

With eyes slightly open, looking at the tip of the nose, chant in a monotone,

HAR HARE (ha-ray) **HARI** (ha-ree) **WHA HAY GURU**

Enunciate clearly, moving the mouth in a very pronounced way (exaggerate the lip movements). Pump the navel point with each part of the mantra (pull the navel point toward the spine). Once you perfect the above, try adding a slight root lock to the pumping of the navel center, which further stimulates the fire in your spine.

HAR HARE HARI are the three aspects of God: Generate, Organize, and Deliver.
WHA HAY GURU means ecstasy and imprints the mind with a feeling of cosmic well-being.

Continue for 31 minutes. This can also be done for 11, 15, or 22 minutes, but for the full effect, do it for 31 minutes for at least 40 days. To install your neutral space, practice for 1,000 days in a row. You will love the results!

To end, hold the position and listen mentally to the mantra for 2 minutes. Then inhale deeply, hold the breath, tense the whole body as tight as you can, exhale. Repeat two more times for a total of three times. Relax on your back or meditate afterwards. Do not jump up immediately.

COMMENTS: This meditation will bring your brainwaves to the frequency of the neutral mind. In the neutral mind, we are tolerant and we don't take things personally. In addition, the meditation opens up the heart chakra and activates the navel center. The mantra has also been given as a prosperity mantra. Like many meditations taught by Yogi Bhajan, there are many benefits that are uncovered as you practice.

The 4/4 Breath for Energy

Sit straight, placing the palms together at the heart center with the fingers pointing up. Focus at the brow point with eyelids lightly closed. While inhaling, break the breath into four equal parts or sniffs, filling the lungs completely on the fourth. As you exhale, release the breath equally in four parts, completely emptying the lungs on the fourth. On each part of the inhale and exhale, pull in the navel point. (The stronger you pump the navel, the more energy you will generate.) One full breath cycle (in and out) takes about 7-8 seconds. Continue for 2-3 minutes. If you press the hands tightly together and pump the navel vigorously, 1 minute will recharge you and alter your mental state. If you are anxious or confused, add the mantra SA TA NA MA mentally on both the inhale and exhale.

To end, inhale, hold, and press the palms forcefully together as hard as you can for 10-15 seconds, creating a tension in the whole body. Hold as long as possible. Exhale powerfully and repeat (inhale, hold, and press). Exhale, relax, and feel all the tension in the body vanish. If you need to rest, immediately lie on the back with the eyes closed and allow each area of the body to relax for 2 more minutes. Take a few deep breaths, stretch, and you will be ready for action.

COMMENTS: Do this meditation during a break in the action or the game. It can rejuvenate coordination and spirit, and possibly prevent injury when playing sports. This is a great quick pick-me-up when you have only a minute. It will relax and energize you and help you combat the encroaching fatigue of emotion. If you do it 2 or 3 times a day at strategic times (before meals, meetings, driving home, etc.) and when you begin to feel tired, you will notice a big difference in the way you feel. Do it at 3:00 p.m. to avoid the "three-o'clock-pass-out syndrome."

STORY: There is a story about Four-Part Breath. Years ago a Kundalini Yoga teacher encountered a man in a wheelchair in the corridor of an office building. He seemed a bit tired. They talked and the teacher shared the Four-Part Breath with him. The next week, the two met again. The man in the wheelchair had a renewed vigor and almost collided with the teacher. As he zoomed by, he extended a warm thank you for the Four-Part Breath.

> Do not spend your spiritual energy on fear. We are at the turning point, the end of Kali Yuga, so all insanity will prevail. Wisdom shall arise from the insanity. Light shall arise from the darkness. Divinity will arise from the chaos. Compassion shall arise from the madness.
>
> – Thich Nhat Hanh, Zen Buddhist Monk

Instant Heart Chakra Opener

On the inhale, whistle "WHEWWWWWWW" for 15 seconds.

On the exhale, chant "LAAAAAAAAAAAAA," moving the "AAA" in waves up the spine, through the chakras, and out the top of the head. Continue for 3-11 minutes.

Chanting Yourself to Sleep
Chanting meditations clears the mind from thoughts about the day. Followed by silent meditation, they promote restful sleep and help you recover from fatigue caused by normal daily stress, travel, and even jet lag. The following meditations are great to do just before you go to bed or whenever you wish to relax and release stress.

COMMENTS: This meditation clears out old energy and thoughts accumulated during the day. It purifies your energy for a restful relaxed sleep. Try it. It works!

Pranayama to Fall Asleep — Chatachya Kriya

In Easy Pose, press heels of hands together and cover left fingers with right fingers, both thumbs touching center section of left Jupiter finger. Place hands 8-10 inches out from the mouth, elbows at sides, eyes closed.

Inhale through the nose and exhale through the mouth, directing the air through the opening in the thumbs. Exhale completely. Practice until you fall asleep.

COMMENTS: This will make you relax and feel good and happy. It will extend your age and make your face innocently charming. Do not practice it if you have work to do, but only if you want to relax or recharge after work. Chatachya refers to making the hands into a little temple.

Shabd Bedtime Meditation

The following meditation is to be done before going to bed. If practiced on a regular basis, every night, or even several times a week, your sleep will be deep and relaxed. The meditation promotes restful sleep and helps you recover from fatigue caused by normal daily stress, travel, and even jet lag. You will think better, work better, share better, and love better.

Directions

MUDRA: Sit in Easy Pose with a straight spine. Hands are in the lap in Buddha Mudra: palms up, right hand resting on top of left. The thumbs touch and point forward.

EYES: The eyes focus at the tip of the nose and are about nine-tenths closed.

BREATH: Inhale in four equal parts (four sniffs) through the nose. Mentally vibrate SA TA NA MA with the four parts of the inhaled breath.

Hold the breath and mentally repeat four repetitions of SA TA NA MA totalling 16 counts:

SA TA NA MA, SA TA NA MA
SA TA NA MA, SA TA NA MA

Then exhale in two equal strokes, mentally projecting

WHA HAY GURU

WHA HAY GURU is translated as ecstasy and is the result of integrating SAT NAM into the psyche. When you experience the Truth, you feel ecstasy.

TIME: Continue for 11, 15, 22, 31, or even 62 minutes. This meditation will often put you to sleep before you complete the allotted time.

COMMENTS: Controlling the rhythm of the breath strengthens the nervous system and regenerates the nerves. After a few months, the rhythm of your breath will be subconsciously regulated, and eventually you will internally chant the mantra while you are sleeping. You may wake up to the internal chant of the mantra and hear it in your daily activities.

Maha Kal Kriya

In Easy Pose, cross wrists over chest, with wrists resting on the chest between the breasts. Maintain a light mahabhand to keep the spine straight and the mind alert to the energy in your spine. With chin pulled in, focus at the top of the head, trying to look at the back of the head. You may feel some discomfort at the sides of the jaws. That's okay.

Vibrate the mantra in the center of the head:

AKAL MAHA KAL
(Undying, great death)

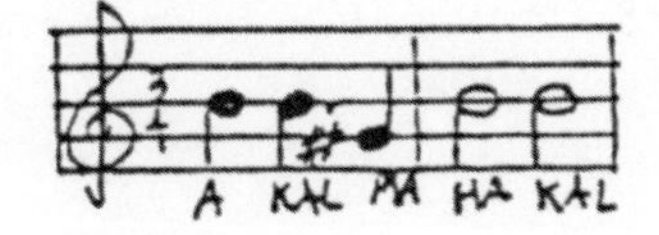

Enunciating each sound — A KAL MA HA KAL — in a monotone.

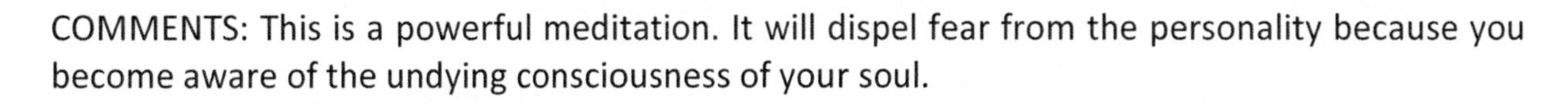

COMMENTS: This is a powerful meditation. It will dispel fear from the personality because you become aware of the undying consciousness of your soul.

Shakti-Bhakti Meditation

Sit in Shakti Posture (Easy Pose, hands in Venus Lock, fingers interlaced, and palms facing down over the solar center on top of the head) and chant for 5-11 minutes

AKAL MAHA KAL

Then in Bhakti Posture (Easy Pose, with both elbows at sides and both hands in Gyan Mudra — women place left forearm straight up, palm facing the face and right forearm straight out, parallel to the ground, palm up. Men reverse with right arm up and left parallel to the ground) with eyes half-closed, again chant for 5-11 minutes

AKAL MAHA KAL

COMMENTS: This meditation produces a peaceful and euphoric feeling. The first position awakens the upper chakras. The second position awakens the heart. Together they make the aura bright and pure, which creates a subtle feel-good experience. Practiced for only 5 minutes (each part) at bedtime induces a blissful and regenerating sleep.

Meditation to Get Out of Depression

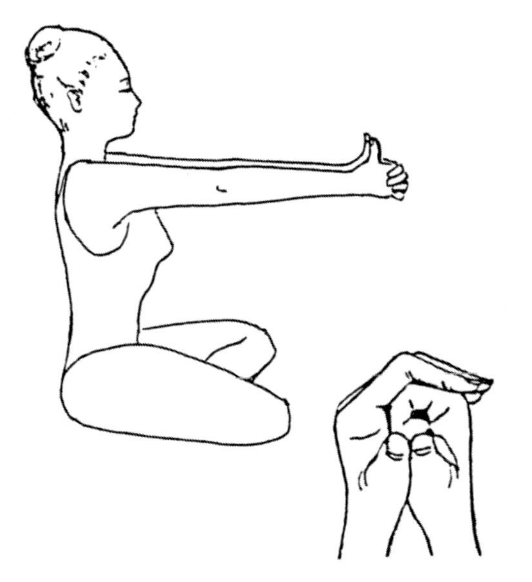

This meditation totally recharges you and is an antidote to depression. It builds a new biochemical system, gives one capacity and caliber to deal with life, and establishes a direct relationship with the pranic body.

Instructions

Sit in Easy Pose or in a chair with a straight spine, extend the arms straight forward, parallel to the ground. Close the right hand in a fist, wrapping fingers of the left hand around it, the bases of the palms touching, thumbs together and pulled up straight. Eyes are focused on the thumbs.

Inhale for 5 seconds, and without holding the breath in, exhale for 5 seconds, and then hold the breath out for 15 seconds. Continue the cycle, starting with 3-5 minutes and working up to 11. Progress slowly. You can also work up to holding the breath out for one full minute. Remember to retain some breath to avoid gasping for air.

Although no mantra is given, you can mentally chant any mantra of your choice. It is handy to chant SA TA NA MA to help keep track of the time.

Student Testimonial:

> I have found this to be a very quick and powerful way to change my emotional state. It seems particularly effective against depression and sadness, and just three minutes can completely alter my state of mind. Another nice thing about this meditation is that it is a quiet one, so I can easily duck into a bathroom stall and, in just a few minutes, raise my consciousness, recover from something trying, and prepare for something new.

> Your biggest weapon is kindness and compassion. That requires intelligence and courage. That requires flexibility and intuition.

Medical Meditation for Habituation

Sit with a straight spine, focusing especially at pushing the lower six vertebrae forward. Make hands into fists, extending the thumbs straight out and placing them on the temples. Lock the molars and rhythmically press them together, feeling the pulsing contractions on the thumbs while chanting

SA TA NA MA

looking to the third eye and feeling the mantra there. Continue for 3-7 minutes, gradually extending the time to 20-31 minutes.

Then place hands on the knees in Gyan Mudra and follow with three repetitions of

AAD GUREY NA MEH
JUGAAD GUREY NA MEH
SAT GUREY NA MEH
SIRI GURU DAY VEY NA MEH

For comfort and protection.

COMMENTS: The thumb pressure triggers a reflex current into the central brain and activates the brain area under the stem of the pineal gland. An imbalance in this area can make physical and mental addictions seem unbreakable, as this imbalance alters radiance in the pineal gland, which regulates the pituitary gland. This meditation is particularly effective for drug dependence, mental illness, and phobic conditions. It is also effective in curbing tobacco, coffee, sugar, and alcohol habits. See "4/4 Breath for Energy" on page 141 for nicotine addiction.

The only thing you can truly give someone is forgiveness. For the sake of giving, forgive. If you have an iota of refined mind, forgive, and forget it. Act from your grace, manners, and awareness, and trust the hand of God. You cannot understand and master the mind without this knowledge of yourself, your reality, and your spirit.

To Break a Drug or Other Addictive Habit

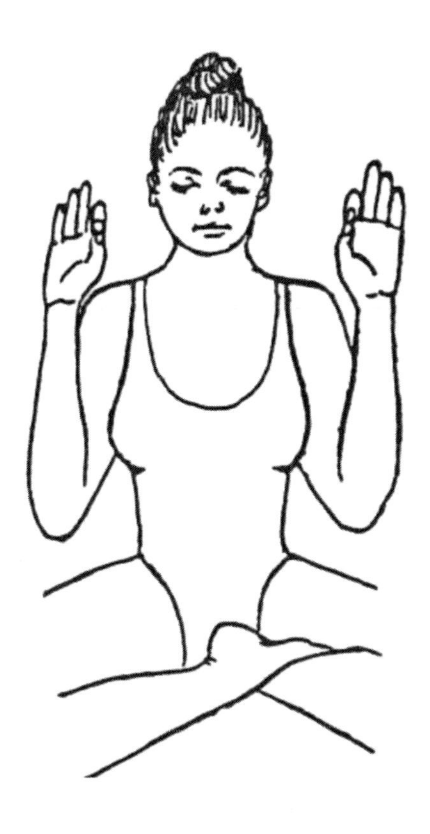

A. Sit with the elbows bent and the forearms up and at the sides, hands in Gyan Mudra, and shoulder blades pressed together in back. Eyes are closed. Inhale and hold the breath in for 1 minute. Exhale and repeat twice.

B. Relax the arms down and breathe normally for 2-3 minutes.

C. Resume the mudra and inhale, pressing the tongue with all your strength against the roof of the mouth and apply root lock for 30 seconds. Exhale and do Breath of Fire for 15-20 seconds. Repeat the sequence one more time.

D. Inhale and press the tongue against the roof of the mouth for 1 minute. Exhale and relax.

COMMENTS: This kriya balances the nervous system and acts as a check on the parasympathetic nervous system. It helps break a drug habit and alleviates withdrawal symptoms. It is an especially good practice for women.

DRUGS: LSD opens the charkas and centers in the brain which are not ready to be open, and then are not properly closed. Yoga must close them. A good practice is "closing the gates." Marijuana affects the "ojas" supplied to the brain. All drugs are a rape of the body. They stimulate certain centers not ready to be stimulated. You are not earning it and must eventually pay the debt.

August 23, 1973

Pranayama to Release Addictive Urges and Thoughts

You can stop an addictive urge by suspending your breath after a deep *inhale*.

The simple formula is

1. Inhale deeply.
2. Suspend the breath and hold for as long as you can. Repeat the following mantra while suspending the breath:

   UNG SUNG WHA HAY GURU

   This mantra means "Ecstasy is alive in every cell of my body."
3. Exhale powerfully.
4. Repeat inhale, suspend, and exhale sequence 7-15 times.

Do this sequence when you feel the urge for a cigarette, drug, drink, sugar, or have a desire that you wish to release. The body's metabolism undergoes a change that substitutes oxygen for nicotine or the need.

Do this routine several times a day when an urge or desire appears that you would like to eliminate. Continue for 40 days or until you are free of the urge or desire.

> Religion is not spirituality. Your knowledge is not spirituality. Your happiness is not spirituality. Your good luck and tragedies are not spirituality. Spirituality is facing yourself with a smile when life confronts you.

Appendix I: Guru Rattana Online Streaming Videos

Videos of some of the kriyas and meditations included in this book can be streamed from Guru Rattana Kundalini Yoga Online at www.yogatech.com/grol.html. It is highly recommended that beginning students who are unable to attend Kundalini Yoga classes in person watch videos of how the exercises, breathing techniques, and meditations are taught by an experienced teacher. More experienced students and Kundalini Yoga teachers in training will also benefit from seeing how Guru Rattana guides her students through the various kriyas and meditations in the videos listed below. First-time users of Guru Rattana Kundalini Yoga Online are entitled to a free preview video. A monthly subscription that provides unlimited access to over 70 professionally filmed and edited yoga videos is available for a small monthly fee.

The first section ***Beginners and Beyond*** will introduce you to all the basics:

- **Introduction — Tune In, The Breath, Sat Nam**
- **Introduction — The Locks & Aligning the Spine**
- **Deepening Our Kundalini Yoga Practice — Part 1**
- **Deepening Our Kundalini Yoga Practice — Part 2**
- **Deepening our Kundalini Yoga Practice — Part 3**
- **Quick Stress Reduction**

The subsequent sections are categorized according to the elements and Sun signs — a great way to find out about yourself and work on issues relevant to your Sun sign. You will discover that all the classes address important life issues.

Testimonial from a Beginning Student

> Your online Kundalini Yoga classes have been an amazing positive addition to my life. I never thought that I could ever do anything like yoga. I grew up having such low self-esteem about my weight and body. I never thought I would ever be flexible enough to practice yoga. I am so delighted that Kundalini Yoga can not only help me physically but, most importantly, help me become spiritually in tune with my inner self.
>
> I enjoy your classes and teachings so so so very much. The classes, learning mantras, learning how to feel the energies inside — the effects are indescribable. I had no idea how vast and abundant my inner self was. I just wanted to start being healthy. I had no clue that being healthy starts within. Words cannot really describe how much I am benefiting from your classes.
>
> Also, I love that I can do yoga in the privacy of my home. I light candles and burn incense every night with my laptop in front of my yoga mat. I feel like I am in the classroom with your other students.

Appendix II:
Guide to Kriyas and Meditations

Something for Everybody!

The wonderful thing about Kundalini Yoga kriyas and meditations is that they all bring harmony to our body and psyche. The list below will help you identify some of the experiences that you can cultivate with the various practices, kriyas, and meditations. Keep in mind that they all work and produce many benefits.

Quick Stress Reduction	Four-Part Breath One-Minute Breath Triangle Pose Alternate Nostril Breathing To Remove Negativity
Quick Energizers	Four-Part Breath Right Nostril Breathing Alternate Nostril Breathing Triangle Pose
Relax and Sleep	Left Nostril Breathing Pranayama to Fall Asleep Instant Heart Chakra Opener Long SAT NAMs Shabd Meditation – Bedtime
Depression Release and Emotional Balance	Right Nostril Breathing Meditation to Get Out of Depression Set to Remove Negativity Heart of Gold All navel exercises Breath of Fire Alternate Nostril Breathing Kirtan Kriya — SA TA NA MA Meditation Basic Breath Series Brainwave Meditation
Get Centered — Mental Clarity	Alternate Nostril Breathing All navel exercises Happy Hips Kirtan Kriya — SA TA NA MA Meditation Nabhi Kriya

	Kriya for Physical and Mental Vitality The Navel Center and Elimination
Awakening Neutral Mind	Tune In Hands out to sides, palms up, Breath of Fire Brainwave Meditation Kirtan Kriya — SA TA NA MA Meditation
Feel Good, Open the Heart	Shakti-Bhakti Meditation Heart of Gold Instant Heart Opener Maha Kal Meditation Brainwave Meditation Set for Strengthening Circulation, the Heart, and Immune System
Eliminate Stress	To Remove Negativity Basic Breath Series Energy and Relaxation for Nerves Instant Heart Chakra Opener
Breaking Habits and Centering	Medical Meditation for Habituation Nabhi Kriya Navel Center and Elimination Kirtan Kriya — SA TA NA MA Meditation Four-Part Breath To Break Drug and Other Addictive Habits Pranayama to Release Addictive Urges/Thoughts
Healthy Back	Spinal Energy Series Kriya for Elevation Spinal Awakening and Centering
Start Your Day	Warm Up Series Spinal Energy Series Spinal Awakening and Centering Sat Kriya Set for Strengthening Circulation, the Heart, and Immune System
Men — Potency	Frog Pose Chair Pose Raise Kundalini in Quick Order Sat Kriya

Women Everyday	Happy Hips Sat Kriya
Moderate Workouts	Spinal Energy Series Kriya for Elevation Spinal Awakening and Centering
Workouts	Navel Center and Elimination Kundalini Kriya #7 Fish Fry Kriya Serabandanda Kriya Raise Kundalini in Quick Order Advanced Kundalini Yoga Kriya #3
End Your Day	Long SAT NAMs Seven-Wave Meditation Left Nostril Breathing Shabd Meditation Pranayama to Fall Asleep
Feel Good	***All of the Above***

♥♥♥

Love to All

Light to All

Peace to All

Guru Rattana, Ph.D.

Guru Rattana earned her Doctorate in Political Science from the Graduate Institute of International Studies (University of Geneva) and received her Master's degree from Johns Hopkins School of Advanced International Studies (Washington, DC, and Bologna, Italy). She has taught International Environment and Development Studies at Dartmouth College, MIT, and New Hampshire College, and Philosophies of Life and History at the U.S. International University. She has also taught at the Institute of Transpersonal Psychology in Palo Alto, California, and at Stanford University.

She is author of four of the original and still globally popular Kundalini Yoga and Meditation manuals: *Transitions to a Heart-Centered World* (2nd edition, 2014), *Relax and Renew*, *Sexuality and Spirituality,* and *Introduction to Kundalini Yoga,* as well as *The Destiny of Women Is the Destiny of the World.* Her most recent books are *The Inner Art of Love, The Gift of Womanhood, The Power of Neutral,* and *Your Life is in Your Chakras* (expanded edition, 2014).

Guru Rattana began studying with Yogi Bhajan in 1977 and is a KRI certified Kundalini Yoga teacher. She has attended over 100 White Tantric Meditation courses, including Summer and Winter Solstices, and over a dozen Khalsa Women's Training Camps, where she has taught many courses.

A pioneering teacher and prolific writer, Guru Rattana has written over 200 issues of the *New Millennium Being* e-zine (now Guru Rattana Blog), featuring insightful articles on spirituality, astrology, and Kundalini Yoga.

Her international teaching tours have included England, France, Sweden, Russia, Ukraine, the Netherlands, Germany, Italy, Turkey, Czech Republic, Switzerland, Portugal, Denmark, Norway, Montenegro, and Croatia, including an annual Gift of Women Retreat. She is lead trainer and co-creator of KRIYA Kundalini Yoga Teacher Training Courses, registered with Yoga Alliance. Guru Rattana lives in Coronado (San Diego), California.

ANN MARIE MAXWELL received her Bachelor of Fine Arts degree from the University of California in Berkeley. A prize-winning artist and writer, Anne Marie is a longtime student of yoga, and one of the original hippies in San Francisco. She danced professionally for 20 years in over 40 cities in the U.S.A. and Canada. She helped create this and three other Kundalini Yoga manuals because she realized that this was the technology for which the flower children of the sixties were really searching.

An Opportunity to Excel

The practice of Kundalini Yoga makes it possible

to transform blocked energy and release our resistance

so that the natural flow of the cosmic current can pass through us

to retrain and rebuild our self

so that we can enjoy the magnificent process of awakening

to develop the discipline and the consciousness

to creatively use our own divine energy.

Kundalini Yoga offers us the opportunity

to go beyond our limited ego imposed limitations that originate from

poor habits

unconscious living

erroneous beliefs.

The practice of Kundalini Yoga gives us the chance

to experience who we already are

to witness Infinity in our everyday lives

to return home to our own heart.

Kundalini Yoga trains us in the inner science of the Self.

It helps us develop a soul relationship with our inner and outer worlds.

It helps us achieve balance and integrity in our feelings and emotions.

It helps us establish synergetic wholeness between body, mind, and Spirit.

In the union of our whole being we achieve

peace of mind

a powerful presence

physical and emotional contentment

effectiveness in our actions

and excellence in our daily lives.

BOOKS BY GURU RATTANA, Ph.D.

Transitions to a Heart-Centered World **(2nd edition, 2014)**
Comprehensive resource of early Kundalini Yoga sets and meditations of Yogi Bhajan, offering powerful techniques to help you open your heart to unconditional love.

Relax and Renew **(2nd edition, 2017)**
Takes stress reduction to the level of holistic resolution. The techniques offered in this book don't just cover up the symptoms — they help cure the problem!

Sexuality and Spirituality **(1989)**
Revolutionary guide to spiritualize sexual energy to enjoy more depth and pleasure in sacred sex and relationships.

Introduction to Kundalini Yoga **Vol. I -** ***Begin and Deepen Your Practice*****; and Vol. II -** ***Inner Awareness and Self-Initiation*** **(2nd edition, 2015)** The fundamentals and benefits of Kundalini Yoga and Meditation.

The Destiny of Women Is the Destiny of the World **(2006)**
An inspiring and invaluable handbook for woman to elevate her consciousness and celebrate her womanhood.

The Inner Art of Love — Awaken Your Heart with Kundalini Yoga **(2011)**
Learn to use the sacred technology of Kundalini Yoga and Meditation to connect with your inner reality, awaken your heart, and become a conscious soul-directed human being.

The Gift of Womanhood — Inner Mastery, Outer Mystery **(2012)**
Reveals woman's mysterious design and guides you to find your authentic identity as a sacred woman, using Kundalini Yoga techniques that awaken your soul.

The Power of Neutral — Soul Alchemy in Meditation **(2013)**
How the mind works, practical ways to direct your meditation practice, keys to awakening and your inner journey.

Your Life Is in Your Chakras **(greatly expanded 2nd edition, 2014)**
Unique collection of information, techniques, and teachings to develop the faculties and gifts of your chakras.

Sing to Your Soul — Awaken to Oneness: Jap-ji Explains the Spiritual Path **(2016)**
Decodes in poetic simplicity the essence of the spiritual journey.

How to Order Your Manuals, Books, DVDs, and CDs

Guru Rattana's manuals and a huge selection of Kundalini Yoga books, DVDs and CDs are available from the Yoga Technology Online Store, http://www.yogatech.com. There you will enjoy very competitive prices and rapid order fulfillment. Special wholesale terms are available for teachers who sign up for our Teachers' Forum.

You can also check out a sample streaming video and sign up for *Guru Rattana Online* Classes, discover a wealth of information about Kundalini Yoga, and read and subscribe to the *Guru Rattana Blog*.

God bless this world
with Peace